CHEMICAL ANALYSIS

Other volumes in preparation

CHEMICAL ANALYSIS

A SERIES OF MONOGRAPHS ON
ANALYTICAL CHEMISTRY AND ITS APPLICATIONS

Volume XI

X-Ray Spectrochemical Analysis
by L. S. Birks

INTERSCIENCE PUBLISHERS, INC., NEW YORK
INTERSCIENCE PUBLISHERS LTD., LONDON

X-RAY
SPECTROCHEMICAL
ANALYSIS

L. S. BIRKS

*X-Ray Optics Branch, U.S. Naval Research
Laboratory, Washington, D.C.*

INTERSCIENCE PUBLISHERS, INC., NEW YORK
INTERSCIENCE PUBLISHERS LTD., LONDON

FIRST PUBLISHED 1959

LIBRARY OF CONGRESS CATALOG CARD NUMBER 59-15341

ALL RIGHTS RESERVED

Interscience Publishers, Inc., 250 Fifth Avenue, New York 1, N.Y.

For Great Britain and Northern Ireland:

Interscience Publishers Ltd., 88/90, Chancery Lane, London W.C.2.

PRINTED IN THE NETHERLANDS

BY DIJKSTRA'S DRUKKERIJ N.V., VOORHEEN BOEKDRUKKERIJ GEBR. HOITSEMA, GRONINGEN

PREFACE

It has been over 25 years since G. von Hevesy's excellent book *Chemical Analysis by X-Rays and its Applications* was published and there has been no other book on the subject during those years. It is not time alone, however, but changes in instrumentation and technique that indicate the need for a new book on x-ray spectrochemical analysis. I have tried to bring the subject up to date for the scientist who is interested in x-ray spectrochemistry as a research tool and also to present the material in a way that will be useful to those persons who are only interested in knowing enough about the method to be able to use it judiciously for routine analysis.

With the knowledge that the majority of readers will not start in and read from cover to cover, I have attempted to arrange the material on excitation, dispersion, detection, and quantitative analysis so that each aspect stands alone. The chapter on applications is intended to point out general types of applications rather than give specific information on a particular subject because there is still rapid change in x-ray spectroscopy, and specific information that is valid today may well be misleading in a few years. Chapter 7 on the electron probe microanalyzer recognizes this new tool as being enough different from fluorescent x-ray spectroscopy to require separate treatment. This is not only because the instrumentation is of a rather different type, but also because the applications will frequently not overlap those of fluorescent analysis.

I wish to express my thanks to E. J. Brooks who has proofread much of the material and made many helpful suggestions during the course of preparation of the manuscript.

Washington, D. C. L. S. Birks
October 1959

FOREWORD

Although x-ray spectrochemical analysis has attained widespread popularity only in the past decade, it is by no means a new field of interest. Study of the x-ray spectral lines and their relation to the chemical elements began shortly after the discovery of x-rays by Röntgen in 1895. In 1911, Barkla and his co-workers showed that characteristic radiation was emitted from an element when it was stimulated by x-radiation of "slightly shorter wavelength" than that which was emitted. Kay, Whiddington, and others soon found that the same characteristic radiation was emitted when the element was made the target in an x-ray tube and bombarded with electrons of sufficiently high energy. In 1913, Moseley began his classical experiments on the relation of wavelength to atomic number and established the simple relation that bears his name: "The frequency of the characteristic lines is proportional to the square of the atomic number." As the theory of atomic structure developed, it was apparent that Moseley's Law was part of the general picture of emission during change in the quantum energy state of an atom.

During the 1920's, von Hevesy and other workers became interested in the use of characteristic x-rays for chemical analysis. Solids or powders to be analyzed were placed on the targets of x-ray tubes and their spectra photographed in x-ray spectrographs using flat calcite crystals to disperse the spectra. A milestone in x-ray spectroscopy was reached in 1923 when Coster and von Hevesy established conclusive proof of the existance of element 72 (Hf) from x-ray spectra of Norwegian zircon. By the 1930's, concentrations of 10^{-4} or 10^{-5} could be measured using suitable standards, and in his book in 1932, von Hevesy stated that he looked forward to the day when concentrations of 10^{-6} could be measured.

The full development of the x-ray method had to wait, however, for technological advances. It was not until the mid 1940's that high-powered, stable, sealed-off x-ray tubes, large single crystals of synthetic rock salt, and sensitive Geiger counters were all brought together to make possible rapid and reproducible measurement of x-ray spectra excited by fluorescence. Great strides have been made in improvements in components and techniques during the past decade with the result that x-ray spectrochemical analysis is now a well established analytical tool that supplements and extends the range of other tools for chemical analysis.

It is the purpose of this volume to try to bring the subject of x-ray spectrochemical analysis up to date and to point out some of its future possibilities.

L. S. B.

CONTENTS

CHAPTER 1

SIMPLIFIED FUNDAMENTALS

1.1. *Relation of Wavelength to Atomic Number*

The following simplified description of fluorescent x-ray spectroscopy will introduce the newcomer to the subject and point out the processes to be considered in detail in succeeding chapters. Before discussing the method, it should be emphasized that the characteristic x-ray spectrum of each element bears a very simple relation to the atomic number. Fig. 1-1 shows the K and L series

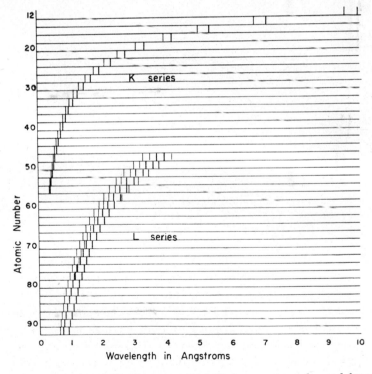

Fig. 1-1. The K and L series x-ray lines that are commonly used for x-ray spectrochemical analysis.

1

lines for the elements from atomic number 11 to 92. The relation of the wavelength, λ, to the atomic number, Z, is given by

$$1/\lambda \propto Z^2 \tag{1-1}$$

where the proportionality constant depends on the series. Because the x-ray lines come from the inner electrons of the atoms, they are not related to any of the chemical properties of the elements nor to the compounds in which they may be present.

1.2.   Geometry of Fluorescent x-Ray Spectroscopy

The simplest arrangement of components for fluorescent x-ray spectroscopy is shown schematically in Fig. 1-2. The main parts

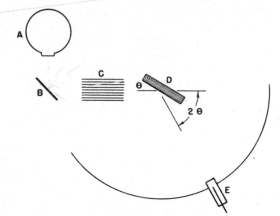

Fig. 1-2. Simple flat-crystal arrangement of components for x-ray spectro-chemical analysis. A, primary x-ray tube; B, specimen; C, collimator; D, analyzing crystal; E, detector.

are A, the primary x-ray tube; B, the specimen; C, the collimator; D, the analyzing crystal; E, the detector. Primary x-rays from the x-ray tube strike the specimen and generate the characteristic x-rays of the specimen elements. The specimen may be a single element such as a sheet of copper, an alloy such as steel, a mixture of powders such as paint pigments, or a liquid containing certain elements in solution. The characteristic x-rays are emitted in all directions and the first step in analysis is to limit them to a parallel bundle with the collimator. As shown in Fig. 1-3, the collimator may be an array of hollow tubes or parallel blades. Next, the parallel bundle of polychromatic radiation strikes the analyzing

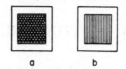

a   b

Fig. 1-3. End view of collimators: a, tube type; b, blade type.

crystal. For each setting of the crystal, only one wavelength will be diffracted according to the Bragg law [1]

$$n\lambda = 2d \sin \theta \qquad (1\text{-}2)$$

where n is the order of diffraction (we will be concerned primarily with the first order: $n = 1$), λ is the wavelength in Angstroms, d is the interplanar spacing of the crystal in Angstroms, and θ is the angle between the incident radiation and the crystal surface as shown. The diffracted radiation emerges at an angle of 2θ with respect to the incident beam and is measured by the detector. To measure the whole spectrum from the specimen, the crystal is turned through $\theta = 0°$ to $\theta = 90°$, and the detector is turned at twice the speed of the crystal so it will always be in position to intercept the diffracted radiation. The wavelengths of the measured x-ray lines determine the elements present in the specimen, and the intensity of each line is related to the percentage composition of that element.

1.3. *Plan of Chapters* 2, 3, *and* 4

We will be concerned in Chapters 2, 3, and 4 with the three processes mentioned above: generation of the x-ray spectra, dispersion according to wavelength, and detection and measurement. Although simple in principle, each of these processes requires care in the choice of equipment and technique if best results are to be obtained.

Reference

1. W. L. Bragg, ed., *The Crystalline State*, Bell, London, 1933.

CHAPTER 2

EXCITATION OF THE X-RAY SPECTRA

Theory of Excitation

2.1. *Production of Continuous Radiation in an x-Ray Tube*

Before discussing the generation of fluorescent x-ray spectra in the specimen, it will be helpful to consider the production of primary x-rays in the x-ray tube. The high-voltage electrons striking the target may lose their energy by either of two processes. Those that knock electrons out of the target atoms generate the characteristic line spectrum of the target element while those that lose their energy by deceleration generate the continuous [1] or "white" radiation.* We will discuss the continuous spectrum first.

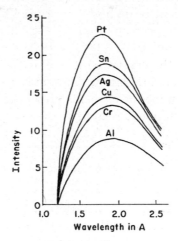

Fig. 2-1. Continuous x-ray spectra from several x-ray target elements all at 15 kev. The intensity of the spectrum depends on atomic number, but the minimum wavelength depends on x-ray tube voltage.

* There is still some question as to exactly how the electrons do lose their energy, and for a more complete discussion, the reader is refered to standard physics texts.

4

Fig. 2-1 shows the spectra for target elements of platinum, tin, silver, copper, chromium, and aluminum from the work of Kulenkampff.[2] Two things are important in Fig. 2-1: all of the spectra have the same minimum wavelength, and the intensity depends on the target element. Both these facts come from well-known physical laws. The minimum wavelength, λ_{min}, depends on the operating voltage, V, of the x-ray tube according to the Duane-Hunt law [3] and is independent of the target element.

$$\lambda_{min} = 12350/V \qquad (2\text{-}1)$$

Eq. 2-1 is merely the standard equation relating quantum energy to frequency but expressed in convenient units. The standard equation is

$$\text{energy} = \hbar\nu$$

where $\hbar$ is Planck's constant and ν is the frequency of the radiation. Frequency is related to wavelength by the velocity of light, c:

$$\nu = c/\lambda$$

The overall intensity of the spectrum, on the other hand, does depend on the atomic number Z. It is ordinarily expressed as I_ν, a function of frequency ν, rather than as a function of wavelength λ.

$$I_\nu = AZ(\nu_0 - \nu) + BZ^2 \qquad (2\text{-}2)$$

where A and B are constants, and ν_0 is the maximum frequency (corresponding to λ_{min}). From Eq. 2-2 and Fig. 2-1, it is apparent that a heavy element target will yield more primary x-rays *of each wavelength* than will a light element target.

2.2. *Production of Characteristic Radiation in an x-Ray Tube*

Characteristic radiation from the target element is produced only when the high-voltage electrons from the filament have sufficient energy to knock out the inner electrons of the target atoms. This energy varies with atomic number and is called the K absorption energy for removal of a K electron or the L absorption energy for removal of an L electron. It is more convenient to express the absorption energy in terms of wavelength as $\lambda_{K\,abs}$ or $\lambda_{L\,abs}$. The minimum potential, V_0, required to excite the K series of the target element is then calculated by substituting the $\lambda_{K\,abs}$ for that element in place of the λ_{min} in Eq. 2-1. For each element, $\lambda_{K\,abs}$ is just shorter in wavelength than the corresponding K emission lines in Fig. 1-1 and $\lambda_{L\,abs}$ is just shorter than the L emission lines. The minimum potential, V_0, for several common target materials is given in Table 2-1.

TABLE 2-1

Minimum Potential Required to Excite the Characteristic Radiation in Common x-Ray Tube Targets

Target	Minimum potential, V_0	x-Ray series
Tungsten	12.1 kev	L
Molybdenum	20.0	K
Copper	9.0	K
Iron	7.1	K
Chromium	6.0	K

Fig. 2-2 shows the characteristic lines of molybdenum superposed on the continuous spectrum [4] at an operating potential of

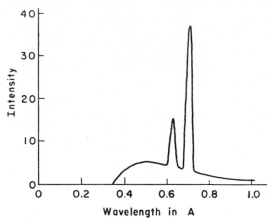

Fig. 2-2. The characteristic K series lines of molybdenum superposed on the continuous spectrum at an operating voltage of 35 kev.

35 kev. The intensity of the characteristic lines increases rapidly as the operating voltage, V, exceeds the minimum voltage, V_0.

$$I \propto (V-V_0)^2 \text{ up to } V \approx 2 \text{ or } 3 \text{ times } V_0 \qquad (2\text{-}3a)$$

$$I \propto V-V_0 \quad \text{for} \quad V > 3V_0 \qquad (2\text{-}3b)$$

Transition from Eq. 2-3a to 2-3b is gradual, and they are intended only to show the approximate relations, not for computing exact values.

2.3. *Excitation of Fluorescent Radiation in the Specimen*

We are now ready to consider fluorescent excitation of the specimen by primary x-radiation from the x-ray tube. For each element, the same energy is required for excitation by fluorescence as for excitation by electrons in Sec. 2.2 above. The minimum operating voltage, V_f, on the primary x-ray tube for exciting an element by fluorescence is expressed according to Eq. 2-1 as

$$V_f = 12350/\lambda_{K\,abs} \qquad (2\text{-}4)$$

Again the intensity of the fluorescent spectra excited increases rapidly as the operating voltage, V, exceeds the minimum voltage, V_f, and the Equations 2-3a and 2-3b may be used with V_f substituted for V_0. V_f depends on the elements to be excited in the specimen, of course, and in practice, an operating voltage well above that required to excite all of the elements of interest is used.

2.4. *Source of the Several Lines in the Characteristic Spectrum of an Element*

The reason for the several spectral lines from an element is illustrated by Figs. 2-3 and 2-4. Fig. 2-3 shows removal of a K electron from an iron atom by a primary x-ray quantum (it does

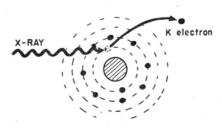

Fig. 2-3. Schematic of the removal of a K electron from an iron atom by a primary x-ray quantum.

not matter whether it be from the continuous or characteristic spectrum). The vacancy may be filled by one of the L or M shell electrons according to certain selection rules.[5] Fig. 2-4 shows

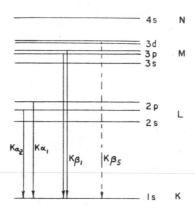

Fig. 2-4. Energy level diagram for iron showing the transitions that correspond to the four lines of the K spectrum. (The separation and position of the energy levels is not to scale.)

schematically an energy level diagram for iron. There are three closely spaced energy levels in the L shell, five in the M shell, and one in the N shell, and they are distinguished in the diagram by standard quantum notation. According to the selection rules, transitions are allowed when the second quantum number, $s = 1$, $p = 2$, or $d = 3$ changes by one. That is, transitions are allowed from the p level of the L or M shell to the s level of the K shell or from the d level of the M shell to the p level of the L shell, etc. If the vacancy in the K shell of Fig. 2-3 is filled by an electron from one of the $2p$ levels, the Fe K_{α_1} or Fe K_{α_2} line is emitted. If it is filled by a $3p$ electron, the Fe K_{β_1} line is emitted. There is also a very weak observed line in the iron spectrum corresponding in energy to transition from the $3d$ level which would be forbidden by the selection rules. On the average, the K_α lines are more likely to occur than the K_β lines, and the relative intensities for the K_{α_1}, K_{α_2}, K_{β_1}, K_{β_5} in iron are 100, 49.1, 18.2, and 0.26.[6] There is some variation in the relative intensities from element to element, but the K_α lines are usually several times more intense than the K_β lines.

2.5. *Source of Background Scattering in Fluorescent Spectra*

It should be noted that no mention has been made of a continuous spectrum excited by fluorescence. *There is no continuous spectrum excited* because the primary x-rays cannot lose their energy in a continuous fashion analogous to the deceleration of electrons in the target of the x-ray tube. What then does cause the low background intensity that is always present in fluorescent x-ray spectroscopy? About half the background intensity is caused by primary radiation scattered by the specimen. Two processes of scattering occur and show up differently in the fluorescent spectrum:

1. Coherent scattering: When an x-ray quantum (photon) strikes an atom, it may, in a sense, "bounce off" without loss of energy, i.e., it is said to suffer an elastic collision. This is the most likely process for those x-ray quanta that do not cause fluorescence and are not absorbed, especially when the specimen is made up of elements of atomic number higher than 11 (Na). The result is the continuous background and weak characteristic primary radiation lines that are almost always observed superposed on the fluorescent spectrum of the specimen. The scattered primary characteristic lines may interfere with an analysis when low concentrations are being measured. For instance, a tungsten target x-ray tube should not be used when low concentrations of tungsten are to be measured in a specimen. The scattered tungsten L spectrum also interferes with the following characteristic lines: the W L_{α_1} line interferes with the Yt L_{β_1}; the W L_{β_2} interferes with the Hg L_{α_2} or Ge K_{α_1}; the W L_γ interferes with the Se K_{α_1}.

2. Compton scattering: When an x-ray quantum strikes an atom, especially an atom of low atomic number such as oxygen, carbon, hydrogen, etc., it may be inelastically scattered and lose part of its energy. This is called Compton scattering,[7] and the loss of energy is dependent on the angle ϕ through which the x-ray quantum is scattered. The loss of energy results in an increase of wavelength, $\delta\lambda$, of the scattered x-ray quantum where

$$\delta\lambda = 0.024(1-\cos\phi) \tag{2-5}$$

For an experimental arrangement such as that shown in Fig. 1-2 of Chapter 1, the angle ϕ between the primary radiation and the scattered radiation that passes through the collimator is about 90° and the value $\delta\lambda$ is about 0.024 A. The result of Compton scattering is a broad maximum on the long wavelength side of each scattered primary characteristic line [8] as shown in Fig. 2-5. In Fig. 2-5, the

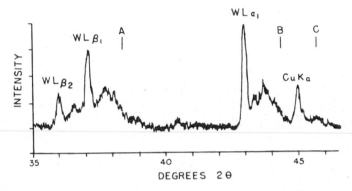

Fig. 2-5. Scattering of tungsten primary x-radiation from a Lucite block. On the long wavelength side of each coherently scattered characteristic line of the tungsten spectrum there is an incoherently (Compton) scattered maximum. The maxima at positions A, B, and C would interfere with the characteristic lines of Ta L_{β_1}, Ta L_{α_1}, and Hf L_{α_1} respectively.

primary radiation from a tungsten target x-ray tube was scattered from a block of Lucite, and the coherently scattered primary characteristic lines show up as rather strong. For a specimen containing mostly hydrocarbons or other very light elements, the Compton scattering will increase relative to the coherent scattering and may even be stronger than the coherent scattering. The Compton scattering in Fig. 2-5 will interfere with measurements of low concentrations of tantalum and hafnium.

As was stated above, about half the background intensity is caused by coherent or Compton scattering of the primary radiation from the specimen. The other half is caused mainly by scattering of the fluorescent radiation from the analyzing crystal. The half scattered from the crystal may be eliminated by pulse amplitude discrimination to be discussed in Chapter 4. The half representing primary radiation scattered from the specimen and diffracted by the crystal according to wavelength cannot be eliminated because it will have the same wavelength as the part of the spectrum on which it is superposed.

Generally speaking, the total background intensity discussed above is not serious for fluorescent x-ray analysis. In fact, the background in the fluorescent spectrum is relatively really very low as compared to that in the primary spectrum, and this favors fluorescent excitation over direct excitation by electrons for the determination of low concentrations.

Operating Conditions

2.6. *Transmission of Primary Radiation by x-Ray Tube Window*

There are several practical considerations in the choice of equipment and techniques for x-ray spectrochemical analysis. Commercial sealed-off x-ray tubes are the most common source of primary radiation. Fig. 2-6 shows both the 100 kev and the 60 kev commercial tubes that are used for fluorescent excitation. The beryllium windows are about 0.030 inches thick and well suited for exciting elements of atomic number greater than 19 (potassium). However, the window transmission falls off rapidly with increasing wavelength and is only 10 % at 3.5 A; 1 % at 4.5 A; 0.1 % at 5.18 A; and 0.01 % at 5.7 A. Thus for elements below phosphorus, less than one part in ten thousand of the most effective x-rays get through the window and are available for exciting the specimen. Even if the window were decreased to 0.010 inches of beryllium, the corresponding transmission would only be extended to 10 % at 5.2 A and 0.01 % at 8.25 A. Inasmuch as the light elements are of increasing interest, here is one of the most important defects in primary x-ray tubes. No easy remedy is envisaged. The best approach appears to be continuously pumped x-ray tubes with the specimen introduced into the tube and excited by fluorescence. A thin Mylar window could be placed between the x-ray tube and a partially evacuated spectrometer so that very little radiation would be lost. In a sense, this would be a throwback to the early days of von Hevesy, but vacuum equipment has improved greatly and commercial instruments of such design may well be feasable.

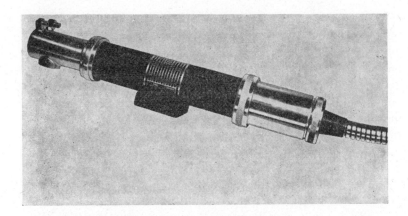

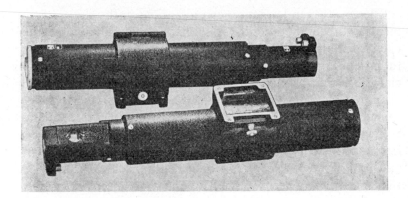

Fig. 2-6. Commercial x-ray tubes used for exciting specimens for fluorescent x-ray spectroscopy. The upper photograph is the Machlett type OEG-50 tube capable of operating up to 60 kev. The lower photograph shows two views of the new Philips tube capable of 100 kev operation.

The problems are not especially more difficult than for electron microscopes and similar instruments.

2.7. *Choice of x-Ray Tube Target Material*

The target material of the primary x-ray tube is of some importance in fluorescent excitation. It is well known from von

Hevesy's work that the most effective wavelength for exciting an element is the wavelength which is about 0.2 A shorter than the absorption edge wavelength for the element (the K edge for exciting the K spectrum, etc.). Thus the Cu K_α line at 1.54 A is very effective in exciting the iron K spectrum with its K absorption edge at about 1.7 A. Likewise, the Mo K_α line at 0.7 A is very effective in exciting the bromine K spectrum or the lead L spectrum in the analysis of leaded gasolines. Because of the rather limited choice of x-ray tube targets, one must usually rely on the continuous primary spectrum to excite the specimen. Then it is wise to choose the target material with the highest atomic number because, as was shown in Sec. 2.1, the intensity of the continuous spectrum increases with atomic number, Z, according to Eq. 2-2. Tungsten is the best all around target material because of its high atomic number and because its high melting point allows a greater tube current to be used. In fact, tungsten is more effective than chromium in exciting the titanium spectrum although the Cr K_α line from a chromium target tube would satisfy the criterion of being the most effective wavelength. This is because a chromium target tube cannot be used at more than one third to one half the current of a tungsten target tube.

There are also situations where the characteristic lines of the x-ray tube target may excite an element that should be suppressed. In the analysis of minor amounts of nickel or cobalt in steel for instance, the strong excitation of the iron K spectrum by a copper target x-ray tube would make it more difficult to measure the weak nickel or cobalt spectra.

2.8. *Effect of x-Ray Tube High Voltage*

Commercial x-ray tubes suitable for fluorescent x-ray spectroscopy were limited to about 60 kev prior to 1956. This determined a minimum wavelength that could be excited according to Eq. 2-1. For 60 kev, the minimum wavelength is 0.206 A. Thus no spectrum may be excited for which the absorption edge is of shorter wavelength than 0.206 A; in practice, the absorption edge should be above 0.3 A because of the rapid fall-off of primary intensity toward the short wavelength limit. The limiting K series spectrum is at about cerium (58) or praseodymium (59). About 1956, x-ray tubes for operation up to 100 kev became available in limited quantities and allowed excitation up to the K spectrum of bismuth (83). One of the most important advantages of the higher voltage is that the K spectra of all the rare earths may be excited, thus eliminating the bothersome overlap of the more numerous L series lines from commonly occuring rare earth mixtures. The shorter wavelengths require scintillation detectors, but these are becoming increasingly more common and are discussed in Chapter 4. It should also be mentioned that the intensity of the K spectral lines of an element is stronger than that of the L spectral lines when sufficient voltage is available. When the K lines of one element fall in the same wavelength range as the L lines of another element, the K lines are about 5 to 8 times stronger than the L lines as shown in Table 6-2 of Chapter 6.

2.9. *Constant Potential High Voltage*

Although the peak voltage on an x-ray tube determines the minimum primary wavelength, the most common method of operating the tube in commercial equipment is with rectified AC potential, which means that the peak voltage is reached only momentarily during each cycle. In Fig. 2-7, the form of the rectified AC voltage is shown with a peak voltage, V_p. Suppose in order to excite the desired element in the specimen, a minimum

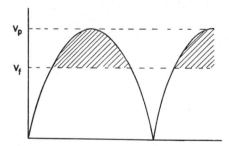

Fig. 2-7. Idealized form of the full-wave rectified AC potential commonly used with commercial x-ray power supplies. If V_f is the minimum potential on the primary x-ray tube that will lead to excitation of the desired characteristic spectrum in the specimen, then only the shaded part of the voltage cycle is effective.

potential on the tube of V_f is required. The only part of the opera-tion cycle that will be effective is the shaded part in the figure, and even then the region just above V_f is not very effective. As was shown in Eqs. 2-3a and 2-3b, the intensity generated increases approximately as the square of the overvoltage $(V-V_f)$ up to about $V = 3V_f$; after that it increases more gradually and ap-proximates a linear relation with overvoltage. Although Eqs. 2-3a and 2-3b are not exact, they may be used to calculate an approxi-mate relation for expected intensities for constant potential (DC) and rectified potential (AC). In Fig. 2-8, the ratio of intensities

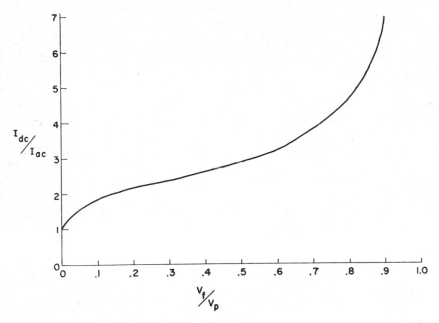

Fig. 2-8. The relative increase in x-ray emission for an x-ray tube operated at constant potential as compared with rectified AC operation. I_{DC}/I_{AC} is the factor of increased emission. V_f/V_p is the ratio of the minimum required voltage to the peak voltage.

I_{DC}/I_{AC} is plotted against V_f/V_p. For the molybdenum K spectrum, V_f is about 20 kev. For a peak operating voltage of 60 kev, $V_f/V_p \approx 0.3$ and from Fig. 2-8 it appears that constant potential would be about $2\frac{1}{2}$ times as effective in exciting molybdenum as the usual rectified AC potential. The advantage of constant potential increases as the minimum excitation voltage, V_f, approaches V_p. In practice it may be necessary to consider the wattage rating of the x-ray power supply as explained in Appendix 1.

Another advantage accrues for constant potential operation. With Geiger counters, there is nonlinearity at high counting rates as will be explained in Chapter 4, Sec. 4.2. With rectified AC operation, the x-ray quanta are generated in only part of the cycle, and for a given *measured* counting rate, with the detector, the real counting rate must have been faster for the effective part of the cycle. Thus linearity losses occur earlier, or saying it another way, the effective dead time of the counter in microseconds is increased. With constant potential operation, the quanta are arriving at the detector at the same rate all the time and this increase in dead time does not occur.

Other Methods of Excitation

2.10. *Excitation by Secondary Fluorescent Radiation*

An aspect of x-ray spectroscopy that has not been investigated extensively is excitation by secondary fluorescent radiation. Suppose for instance, we wish to excite iron in some matrix. Why not first excite copper with primary radiation and then use the fluorescent copper characteristic lines to excite the iron? This certainly can be done, but the total intensity of the copper characteristic lines will be far less than the total intensity of the primary radiation in the effective wavelength range. Thus the excitation of the iron will be far less than by using the primary radiation directly. However, there may be cases when intensity may be sacrificed for a clean spectrum. For instance, if we wish to measure chromium in the presence of cobalt, a secondary iron radiator would be a suitable choice because Fe K_α would be very efficient in exciting the chromium but of insufficient energy to excite the cobalt. Nondispersive x-ray optics, described in Sec. 0.0, could be used because the only radiation being emitted in the specimen would be the chromium spectrum. Second-order effects such as some cobalt radiation being excited by scattered primary radiation would be present but of very low intensity. It remains for workers in the field to find suitable problems where secondary fluorescent excitation will be of advantage.

2.11. *Electron and Alpha Particle Excitation*

The foregoing sections have been concerned with fluorescent excitation of the specimen by x-rays, and this is by far the most common method in present day equipment. However, electrons and alpha particles are effective in exciting the specimen and should not be overlooked. The electron probe,[9] which uses electron excitation, is a promising tool for x-ray spectrochemical analysis and is described in Chapter 7. Electron excitation is actually much more efficient than fluorescent excitation.[10] For instance, the intensity of CuK_α is several hundred times greater when the copper is the x-ray tube target than when a copper specimen is excited by fluorescence outside the tube. However, with electron excitation the background level is increased even more proportionally than the line, and the minimum concentration detectable in a specimen is often less because of the poor line-to-background ratio. It is primarily the inconvenience of electron excitation, however, that limits its use.

For light elements such as potassium and chlorine, alpha particles sometimes offer a convenient and efficient means of excitation.[11] Thin sheets of plastic such as Saran, which contains chlorine, will absorb the alpha particles from a polonium source whereas x-rays or electrons would pass through and not excite the atoms in the film. *Use of active alpha particle sources can be dangerous and appreciable caution is required.*

References

1. J. D. Stranathan, *The Particles of Modern Physics*, Blackiston, Philadelphia-Toronto, 1942, p. 294.
2. H. Kulenkampff, *Ann. Physik.* **69**, 548 (1922).
3. W. Duane and F. L. Hunt, *Phys. Rev.* **6**, 166 (1915).
4. C. T. Ulrey, *Phys. Rev.* **11**, 401 (1918).
5. A. H. Compton and S. K. Allison, *X-rays in Theory and Experiment*, Van Nostrand, New York, 1935, p. 629.

6. M. Siegbahn, *Spectroskopie der Röntgenstrahlen*, Springer, Berlin, 1931.
7. See Ref. 5, p. 48.
8. E. J. Brooks and L. S. Birks, *Anal. Chem.* **29**, 1556 (1957).
9. R. Castaing, *Thesis*, University of Paris, (1951).
10. Wm. Parrish, *Philips Tech. Rev.* **17**, 269 (1956).
11. H. Friedman, *Pittsburgh Conf. on Analytical Chemistry and Applied Spectroscopy*, Paper No. 56, (1956).

CHAPTER 3

DISPERSION AND GEOMETRY

3.1. *Introduction*

Once the characteristic x-ray spectrum of the specimen has been excited, it is necessary to distinguish the various wavelengths. This is done either by dispersive x-ray optics using analyzing crystals or by nondispersive optics making use of the different energies of the different lines. The dispersive systems offer far better resolution of course and will be described first. Four dispersive geometries have been found useful and are designated as flat crystal, curved reflection crystal, curved transmission crystal, and edge crystal. Before discussing these four geometries, however, a few facts concerning the analyzing crystals themselves should be mentioned.

Crystals

3.2. *Diffracted Intensity for Various Crystals*

The analyzing crystal might be called the heart of the x-ray spectrometer. Both intensity and resolution are controlled by the crystal's properties. An improvement by a factor of two in primary x-ray tube power is considered extraordinary and is expensive in terms of equipment and design, but an improvement by a factor of two in crystalline diffracting power serves the same purpose and is often easier to obtain. A truly perfect crystal would give very low diffracted intensity because of primary extinction, and would be of almost no use as an analyzing crystal. Natural and synthetic crystals vary in their imperfections; the ideally imperfect crystal contains mosaic blocks of the order of 10^{-5} cm in size and misoriented with respect to each other by not more than a few minutes of arc.[1] As is explained in texts on crystallography, this reduces the primary extinction and makes for far greater diffracted intensity.

19

The alkali halides such as LiF, NaCl, and KCl that are commonly used in fluorescent x-ray spectroscopy fall into the ideally imperfect class of crystal. Quartz is somewhat more perfect than the alkali halides but may be rendered more mosaic and have its diffracting power increased by abrading the surface. A number of calculations of expected intensity of diffraction have been made for various crystals based on the known electron scattering factors and certain assumptions about the atoms comprising the crystal.

TABLE 3-1

Calculated x-Ray Diffraction Intensity from Several Common Crystals

Crystal	Diffracting planes	Calculated intensity
Graphite	(002)	500
Pentaerythritol	(002)	115
Lithium fluoride	(200)	110
Diamond	(111)	85
Copper	(200)	70
Quartz	(101)	43
Sodium chloride	(200)	30–45
Aluminum	(200)	30

Table 3-1 shows values calculated by R. Renninger for some of the more common crystals.[2] These values have been found to be in fair agreement with experiment for untreated crystals. For a given crystal, deliberate introduction of elastic or plastic strain usually increases the diffracted intensity without excessive broadening of the diffracted line. In fact White[3] showed an increase of as much as 20 times in the integrated diffraction line from elastically strained quartz. Birks and Seal[4] showed that plastic strain in LiF increased the peak intensity of the diffracted line by from 4 to 10 times. Metal crystals such as aluminum are favored by some workers and give intensities comparable with those from untreated alkali halides as shown in Table 3-1.

3.3. *Crystalline Interplanar Spacing and Relation to Wavelength*

A second consideration in the choice of crystal is the interplanar spacing. From the Bragg law

$$n\lambda = 2d \sin \theta$$

it is immediately apparent that the maximum wavelength that may be diffracted is equal to $2d$. Thus LiF with $2d = 4.02$ A is useful only down to the K lines of potassium (19) at 3.7 A. The $(10\bar{1}0)$ planes of quartz with $2d = 8.5$ are useful down to the K lines of aluminum (13) at 8.3 A. Thus as we go to the lower atomic number elements, it is necessary to find suitable crystals of greater d spacing. While it is known that many crystals of long spacing such as oxalic acid dihydrate ($2d = 11.7$ A) or silver acetate ($2d = 20$ A) give very strong diffraction, it has not been possible to grow them in sufficient size to be useful as analyzers. Perhaps the most suitable crystal at present for the aluminum to phosphorous wavelength range is ethylenediamine d-tartrate (EDDT) with $2d = 8.76^2$A. It does not have the diffracting power of the alkali halides but does give usable intensities. Mica has a satisfactory spacing for sodium and magnesium but is relatively quite weak in diffracted intensity. Undoubtedly the organic chemists will be able to "design" crystals of suitable spacing and high diffracting power in time, but at present, this is one of the limiting factors in the analysis of light elements.

One point should be mentioned in connection with long spacing crystals. From the Bragg law, it is obvious that a long spacing crystal will diffract the short wavelengths as well as the long wavelengths. It is best, however, to choose the shortest spacing that will diffract the required wavelengths. This is because the dispersion, $d\theta/d\lambda$, increases as the spacing decreases. Thus for short spacing crystals, neighboring wavelengths will be further separated in angle and so better resolved. This is seen by differentiating the Bragg law to obtain

$$d\theta/d\lambda = n/2d \cos \theta$$

As d decreases, $d\theta/d\lambda$ increases because $\cos \theta$ is always less than unity. The separation of Cr K_β and Mn K_α is 0.25° θ with LiF as compared with 0.16° θ for quartz (taking into account the proper value of $\cos \theta$).

Flat Crystal Geometry

3.4. *Arrangement of Equipment and Shape of the Diffracted Lines*

Flat crystal geometry is perhaps the simplest for x-ray spectroscopy and was shown schematically in Fig. 1-2 of Chapter 1. One of its characteristics is that for each setting of the crystal at some angle θ_i, radiation of wavelength λ_i, satisfying the Bragg equation, from all parts of the specimen is diffracted and passed along to the detector in a parallel bundle. This means two things: inhomogeneities in the specimen are averaged out; and the whole volume of the detector must be sensitive if optimum use is to be made of the broad beam striking it. The purpose of the collimator is to allow only a parallel bundle of the polychromatic radiation from the specimen to strike the crystal. Resolution is limited by the divergence allowed by the collimator and by the rocking curve of the crystal. The intensity passing through a collimator has a triangular distribution with angle as shown in Fig. 3-1b, and the

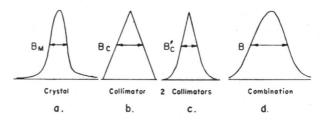

Fig. 3-1. Distribution of x-ray intensity with angle. The rocking curve for the crystal will be broadened by the divergence of the collimator to give a distribution curve that is a combination of the two. The breadth of the combination curve is given by Eq. 3-1 in the text.

breadth at half maximum is B_C. The breadth B_C is determined by the length, L, of the collimator and the spacing, s, between blades according to the equation

$$B_C = \text{arc tan } (s/L)$$

The intensity that would be diffracted by the crystal from a strictly parallel beam of incident radiation is represented by the Gaussian rocking curve of Fig. 3-1a. The breadth at half maximum, B_M, depends on the mosaic structure of the crystal.

When a single collimator is used, the diffracted x-ray line breadth is obtained from the convolution of the crystal rocking curve and the collimator divergence. By assuming the collimator divergence to approximate a Gaussian distribution, the final breadth, B, is obtained from the breadths B_M and B_C by the usual rule for adding variance and is shown as the first line in Eq. 3-1.

If a second collimator of the same divergence as the first is inserted between the crystal and detector of Fig. 1-2 of Chapter 1, the crystal rocking curve has little effect on the diffracted line breadth which is now obtained by squaring each ordinate of Fig. 3-1b to obtain Fig. 3-1c. The breadth of the squared curve $B_{C'}$ is approximately $0.6B_C$ and this is equal to the diffracted line breadth as shown in the second line of Eq. 3-1.

$$B^2 = B_M^2 + B_C^2 \text{ for 1 collimator}$$
$$B \approx 0.6B_C \text{ for 2 collimators} \tag{3-1}$$

For LiF crystals, B_M will be about $0.2°$ and B_C will be about $0.07°$ for a 4-inch long collimator with 0.005 inch spacing. Thus B for a single collimator will be about $0.21°$, only a slight increase over the rocking curve for the crystal. For a more perfect crystal such as quartz, B_M may be as low as $0.05°$; B_C remains unchanged, and B_C' is $0.6 B_C$. For a single collimator then B will be $0.085°$ and for two collimators, B will be $0.042°$, an improvement of about 50 %.

3.5. *Comparison of Blade and Tubular Type Collimators*

Collimators usually consist of parallel blades or a close packed array of tubings as shown in Fig. 1-3 of Chapter 1. With the tubes, divergence is limited in both directions. A comparison of the two types of collimators is shown in Fig. 3-2. For each spot on the crystal, the Bragg angle is satisfied for a cone of semi-angle $90° - \theta$. Although the divergence allowed in the plane of the spectrometer is the same for either type of collimator, the divergence in the plane perpendicular to the plane of the spectrometer is much greater for the blade system. This perpendicular divergence is directly related to h_1, the diameter of the tubes and to h_2, the height of the blades. For typical values of $h_1 = \frac{1}{16}$ inch and $h_2 = \frac{3}{4}$ inch, the

increase in divergence using blades is about 12 times with a corresponding increase in intensity. The advantage of blades decreases as θ approaches 90° because not all the perpendicular di-

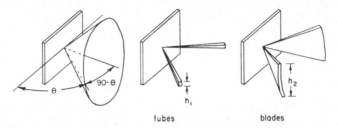

tubes   blades

Fig. 3-2. The idealized full cone of diffraction is limited to the segment h_1
by a tubular collimator, or to h_2 by a blade type collimator.

verging radiation satisfies the Bragg angle for diffraction at the
same crystal setting as shown in Fig. 3-3. The dotted outline represents the height and separation of the blades and is seen to cut

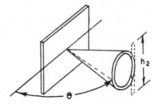

Fig. 3-3. At high θ angles, only a small part of the radiation in the diffraction cone will be passed by a blade type collimator, and the blade type
loses its advantage over the tubular type.

only a small arc of the cone of diffraction. For $\theta = 80°$, not much
more than 10 % of the perpendicular divergence is effective, and
almost all the advantage of the blades is lost. Besides the loss of
intensity at high θ angles, the line is broad and asymmetric with
a blade collimator because of later diffraction of the more divergent
radiation.

A different type of problem arises for small values of θ. As can be
imagined in Fig. 1-2 of Chapter 1, as θ decreases, the crystal is not
long enough to intercept all of the radiation emerging from the
collimator. If the full width of the collimator is b, the length of the

crystal, l, required to intercept all of the beam is easily seen to be $l = b/\sin\theta$. For b equal to 1 inch and l equal to 3 inches, the limiting value of θ for complete interception is 19.4°. Intensity will fall off for smaller values of θ. It is impractical to increase l beyond about 4 inches and a corresponding value of $\theta = 14.5°$. It becomes of advantage to use a thin flat crystal in transmission for low θ values. LiF with its low absorption coefficient has an optimum thickness in transmission of almost 3 mm for Mo K_α radiation and almost twice as much radiation is intercepted as with a three inch long crystal in reflection. For shorter wavelengths than Mo K_α, the situation is even more favorable for transmission. It is a little troublesome to convert commercial spectrometers to mount transmission crystals but for special problems it may be of sufficient advantage to do so.

Curved Reflection Crystal Geometry

3.6. *Conditions of Curving and Grinding for Focusing Geometry*

Cylindrically curved crystals may be used in x-ray spectroscopy to diffract and "focus" radiation diverging from a line or point source as shown in Fig. 3-4a. The circle along which "focusing" occurs is the same Rowland circle as in conventional optics. The curved crystal acts in an analogous manner to the concave gratings used in ordinary emission spectroscopy. Of course, the crystal does not focus x-rays in the optical sense but merely diffracts them in such a manner that they converge to a line image. To understand the geometry of curved crystal x-ray optics, it is easiest to consider the crystal to be made up of short, discrete segments along the focusing circle and to refer to Fig. 3-4b. Let A and C be the source and image points respectively and let B be half way between. We will call the angle of diffraction θ as usual, and it will be the angle between the line AB and the tangent at B and likewise between the line CB and the tangent. Thus Bragg's law is satisfied for crystal planes tangent to the circle at B. It is easily shown that the angle AOB is 2θ; the proof is as follows: let angle AOB be called γ temporarily. Since triangle AOB is isosceles, angles OBA and OAB are each equal to $(180-\gamma)/2$. But the angle

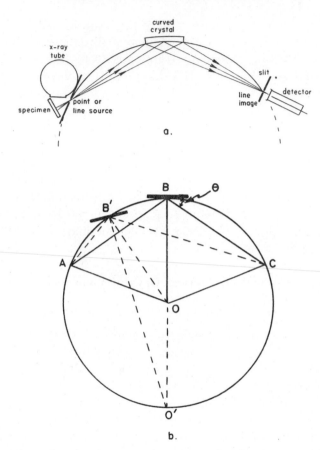

Fig. 3-4. Curved, reflection crystal, x-ray optics. In the upper drawing, radiation from a point or line source diverges to the curved crystal, is diffracted, and converges to a line image on the focusing (Rowland) circle. In the lower drawing, the center of curvature for the crystal must be at position O′ rather than at position O; that is, the crystal is curved to a radius equal to the diameter of the focusing circle.

between the line OB and the tangent is $90°$ and therefore $OBA = 90° - \theta$. Substituting, we find $90° - \theta = (180° - \gamma)/2$ giving $\gamma/2 = \theta$ or $\gamma = 2\theta$.

Now consider the point B' such that angle AOB' and $B'OB = \theta$. By reasoning from the preceding paragraph, the angle between line AB' and the tangent to the circle at B' will be $\theta/2$. But for diffraction, the angle must be θ. Therefore the crystal planes must be turned clockwise by an amount $\theta/2$ and the normal to the planes likewise. The normal to the diffracting planes at B' will strike the circle at O' and again by the rule of isosceles triangles, angles $OB'O' = \theta/2 =$ angle $OO'B'$. The only way for angle $B'O'B$ to be equal to $\theta/2$ and angle $B'OB$ to be equal to θ, is for $O'B$ to be a diameter of the circle. For any other point between A and C it can also be shown that the normal to the diffracting planes must pass through the same point O', and O' is therefore the center of curvature for each segment of the crystal. In a real crystal this can be satisfied by bending a long crystal to a radius equal to the diameter of the focusing circle. Of course it will not lie along the circle then but may be made to do so by grinding the inner surface of the crystal to the radius of the focusing circle. These then are the familiar Johansson conditions [5]—curving to the diameter of the focusing circle and grinding to the radius.

3.7.   Effects of Curving and Grinding Errors

Either plastic or elastic curving may be used in practice. Plastic curving is better suited to alkali halides and elastic curving to quartz and similar materials. An error in the value of the bending

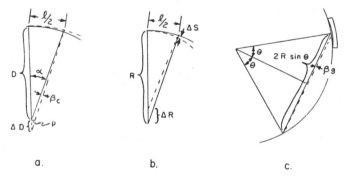

a.   b.   c.

Fig. 3-5. Errors introduced in curved reflection optics by an improper curving or grinding radius. For an error in curving radius of ΔD, the error angle at the end of the crystal will be β_c. For an error in grinding radius of ΔR, the end (or center) of the crystal will lie off the focusing circle by a distance ΔS. When the crystal does not fit the focusing circle, an error in angle of β_g is introduced.

radius will have more serious consequences than an error in the value of the grinding radius and may be more difficult to eliminate especially with plastically curved crystals. Fig. 3-5a illustrates the effect of an improper bending radius. Suppose the desired radius of curvature is $2R = D$, but the actual value obtained is $D + \Delta D$. This may happen in plastic curving if the crystal springs back slightly after being formed to the die. The center of the crystal is unaffected of course, but the error in angle at the outer end of the crystal is β_c. The diffracted line will be broadened by an amount β_c. Simple trigonometry gives the following relations

$$\beta_c = p/D \qquad (3\text{-}2a)$$

$$p = \Delta D \times \alpha \qquad (3\text{-}2b)$$

$$l/2D = \alpha \qquad (3\text{-}2c)$$

Substituting Eqs. 3-2c and 3-2b into Eq. 3-2a, the error angle β_c becomes

$$\beta_c = l/2 \times \Delta D/D^2 \qquad (3\text{-}3)$$

Substituting commonly used values of $l = 2$ inches $= 5.08$ cm, $D = 20$ cm, $\Delta D = 0.5$ cm, the error angle or broadening, β_c, becomes 0.00313 radians $= 0.18°$; for LiF crystals, this value is smaller than the diffraction line breadth and indicates that usually no difficulty will be experienced in preparing plastically curved crystals. For quartz or more perfect crystals a broadening of $0.18°$ would be serious however and more care is required in curving.

Grinding errors have a somewhat different effect as shown in Fig. 3-5b. For an error ΔR in the grinding radius, the end of the ground crystal will be off the focusing circle by a distance ΔS where

$$\Delta S = \beta \times l/2 \qquad (3\text{-}4a)$$

and

$$\beta = l/2 \times \Delta R/R^2 \qquad (3\text{-}4b)$$

The error angle β_g is

$$\beta_g = \Delta S \cos \theta / 2R \sin \theta \qquad (3\text{-}4c)$$

Substituting Eqs. 3-4a and 3-4b into Eq. 3-4c, the error angle β_g becomes approximately

$$\beta_g = l^2 \Delta R / 8R^3 \tan \theta \qquad (3\text{-}5)$$

Again putting in commonly used values of $l = 2$ inches $= 5.08$ cm, $R = 10$ cm, $\Delta R = 0.1$ cm, $\theta = 20°$, the error angle β_g becomes 0.000872 radians $= 0.05°$ or less than $\frac{1}{3}$ that of curving.

3.8.   Two Types of Curved-Crystal Spectrometers

The mechanics of positioning the curved crystal and detector may be accomplished in several ways, two of which are shown in Fig. 3-6. Figs. 3-6a and c show the arrangement used by Birks and Brooks,[7a] and Fig. 3-6b and d show the arrangement in the equipment developed by Applied Research Laboratories.[7b] In Fig. 3-6c, the axis of the focusing circle is fixed with respect to the specimen slit. The crystal and detector are mounted on separate arms and turned by concentric shafts. Of course the detector arm must turn at twice the rate of the crystal arm so the detector will always be in position to intercept the diffracted radiation. The detector must also be kept pointed towards the crystal rather than tangent to the circle. In order to keep it pointed towards the crystal, it is fixed on a circular plate that is free to rotate in its mount on the end of the detector arm. A pulley, half the diameter of the circular plate, is fixed to the crystal arm shaft and connected to the circular plate by a wire as shown. As the crystal and detector arms turn, the pulley arrangement rotates the circular plate in the opposite direction at half the rate of the detector arm motion. Thus, as the crystal arm turns from zero to 45°, the detector arm turns from zero to 90° but the circular plate is turned backwards by 45° as shown in the figure. The advantage of this type of spectrometer is that it is very compact and the drive mechanism is very simple. The disadvantage is that the specimen must be homogeneous because the crystal "sees" successively different areas of the specimen surface through the specimen slit as the θ angle is changed.

In the arrangement shown in Fig. 3-6d, the crystal is restrained to move along a straight line away from the specimen slit. As it moves through positions a, b, c, the focusing circle effectively swings about the specimen slit as shown. The detector moves along a noncircular path cut in a metal plate and is kept pointed

towards the crystal by a sliding guide rod through the crystal and
detector mounts.* The advantage of this arrangement is that the
crystal continues to "see" the same area on the specimen surface

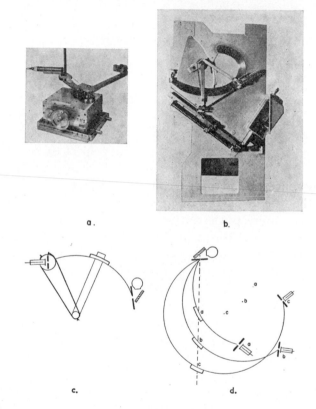

Fig. 3-6. Scanning curved-crystal spectrometers, a and c, Naval Research
Laboratory design; the center of the focusing circle remains fixed with the
crystal and detector moving along the periphery of the circle; b and d,
Applied Research Laboratories design: the crystal moves in a straight line
while the center of the focusing circle swings through positions a, b, c, etc.;
the detector is constrained to move along an eccentric path to positions
a, b, c, etc.

* The path along which the detector moves is called a fourleafed-rose
curve in analytical geometry and has the equation $\rho = 2R \sin 2\theta$ where R
is the radius of the focusing circle and θ is the diffraction angle.

as it moves away from the slit. Mechanically this type of arrangement is more complicated and requires more space.

3.9. *The Use of a Point or Line-type Specimen*

When a point or line specimen is used, in order to reduce air scattering, the primary x-ray beam should be masked down so that only the specimen is irradiated. A one milligram capillary type specimen acting as a line source on the focusing circle yields approximately the same intensity as a large flat specimen and slit.[7a] This is because a large solid angle of radiation from the small line area is utilized with a capillary specimen as compared with a very small solid angle (the angle subtended by the source slit) from a number of line areas in the flat specimen. In fact, the intensity may even be increased with a capillary specimen because the x-ray tube may be moved closer to the specimen to excite it more strongly. By concentrating a small amount of specimen material in a small circle, say $\frac{1}{2}$ mm in diameter, it is possible to obtain useable intensities from as little as 10^{-8} grams of an element acting as a point source. Alternatively, it is also possible to mask the primary beam with a lead cone and irradiate only a $\frac{1}{2}$ mm circle on a large flat specimen. If the specimen is positioned so this irradiated area acts as a point source on the focusing circle, variation in composition across the surface may be measured by translating the specimen in front of the lead cone. Applications for the masking

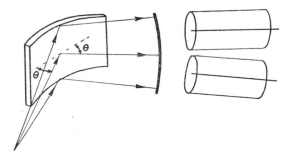

Fig. 3-7. In curved reflection optics, radiation diverging from a point source will converge to a line image rather than a point image after diffraction.

technique include inhomogeneous mineral specimens,[8] diffusion regions, weld beads, etc., (see Chapter 6).

With either a point source or a line source, the image will be a line as shown in Fig. 3-7. With a crystal 1 inch high, the line will be 2 or 3 inches high except at very large θ angles, and it is profitable to use two detectors to intercept more of the radiation.

3.10. *Intensity and Resolution as Compared with Flat-Crystal Geometry*

Intensity and resolution are similar for the curved reflection crystal and the flat crystal arrangements provided there is no change in x-ray tube operating conditions, specimen size, or the distance from specimen to crystal and crystal to detector. At large θ angles, the same loss of resolution occurs due to perpendicular divergence. Background intensity may be made somewhat lower with the curved crystal than with the flat crystal by placing a coarse slit in front of the detector at the image point on the focusing circle as shown in Fig. 3-4. This slit passes all the radiation in the line image but stops scattered radiation that would otherwise enter the detector.

Doubly Curved Crystals

3.11. *Preparation and Limitations*

Doubly curved reflection crystals may be used to focus radiation diverging from a point source back to a point image provided the wavelength is just right. Referring back to Fig. 3-4, imagine the figure of revolution obtained by rotating the arc of the focusing circle about the chord joining the source and image. If the crystal is curved to fit this surface after first bending to the diameter of the focusing circle, the image will be a point rather than a line.[9] Such double curving is possible with plastically deformed crystals but the resulting crystal will be proper for only one wavelength. For other wavelengths, the second curvature will be of improper radius and a line image will be obtained. It is also possible to use thin slices of cylindrically curved crystals arranged on the figure of revolution surface to approximate the doubly curved crystal.[10] The sections may be rearranged for various wavelengths, but this does not lend itself readily to scanning through a spectrum. It should be mentioned that doubly curved crystals are more valuable in x-ray diffraction where one is interested in only a single wavelength.

Transmission Curved Crystals

3.12. *Use for Point Source and Extended Source of Radiation*

Cylindrically curved crystals may be used in transmission arrangements as shown in Fig. 3-8. In this case, the planes perpendicular to the crystal surface are used for diffraction rather than

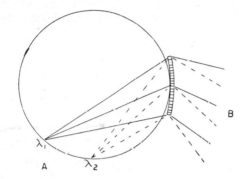

Fig. 3-8. Curved transmission x-ray optics. Two types of use are possible. Polychromatic radiation from a broad source at *B* will be diffracted and dispersed so that a line spectrum of the various wavelengths is formed on the focusing circle. On the other hand, if a polychromatic line or point source is located on the focusing circle in region *A*, only one wavelength will be diffracted selectively by the crystal, and the diffracted radiation will continue to diverge into the space *B*.

the planes parallel to the surface. Again the radius of curvature is equal to the diameter of the focusing circle. No grinding of the crystal is necessary however. The interesting feature of this type of crystal is that it may be used in two different ways. If a large source of fluorescent x-radiation such as a flat specimen is used in the *B* position in Fig. 3-8, the various wavelengths will be diffracted to specific points along the focusing circle. On the other hand, if a point source of radiation is located on the focusing circle at the

A position, only one wavelength will be diffracted selectively by the crystal and the diffracted radiation will continue to diverge. This latter arrangement is used to advantage with the electron probe discussed in Chapter 7.

Edge Crystal Geometry

3.13. *Simultaneous Recording of the Complete Spectrum*

The final dispersing system will be called the *edge* crystal,[11] and the geometry is shown in Fig. 3-9. The planes parallel to the thin edge are used for diffraction, and the breadth of each diffracted line is just the width of the edge projected onto the circle. Crystals as thin as 0.005 inches may be prepared from LiF and

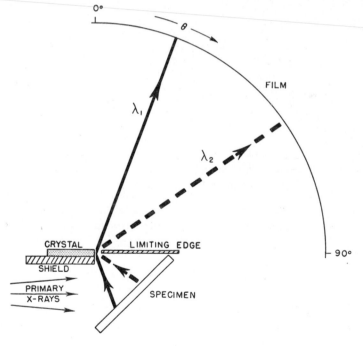

Fig. 3-9. Edge crystal geometry. Planes parallel to the thin edge of the crystal diffract the whole spectrum at one time, but each wavelength must arise from a different portion of the specimen; thus a homogeneous specimen is required for quantitative analysis.

resolution of $Cr\,K_\beta$ and $Mn\,K_\alpha$ obtained. Each wavelength diffracted arises from a different portion of the specimen; thus a
homogeneous specimen is required so that each wavelength will
be properly represented quantitatively. The advantage of the
edge crystal geometry is that no moving parts are required and an
extremely simple spectrograph may be constructed. The complete
spectrum is recorded at one time on photographic film placed
along the arc of the circle and the total time for recording a complete spectrum compares favorably with more elaborate spectrometers. A standard specimen spectrum may be recorded side by
side with the unknown for easy comparison. The only disadvantage
is that the photographic density of the lines on the film cannot be
related to incident intensity as accurately as the intensity can be
measured with a Geiger counter or other detector for quantitative
analysis. Of course with scanning spectrometers, it is possible to
measure just a few lines and so save time over recording the whole
spectrum when only a few elements are to be determined.

Automatic Instruments for Rapid Analysis

3.14. *Simultaneous Analysis with Fixed Crystals and Detectors
Sequential Analysis with a Single Spectrometer*

All of the geometries described in this chapter were first developed for what might be called research-type instruments. Usually
motorized scanning and strip-chart recording are used for qualitative or semi-quantitative analysis, but for accurate quantitative
analysis, the spectrometer must be set for a particular wavelength
and a measurement made of the total number of x-ray quanta
arriving in a known time interval. When several elements are to be
determined, a semi-skilled operator is required to set the spectrometer properly at each line-peak and background position, com-
pute the counting rate, and compare the measured intensities with
those obtained from known standards. For large-scale repeated
measurements in industry, this is not economically profitable and
more automatic instrumentation is desirable. Two methods of
automatic measurement have been incorporated in commercial
x-ray spectrometers.

Method A [7b] is shown schematically in Fig. 3-10. The specimen is placed near an end-window primary x-ray tube and as many as 23 crystals and detectors set at fixed positions in a circle around

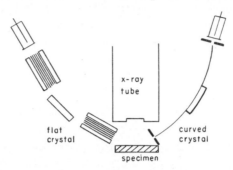

Fig. 3-10. Arrangement for simultaneous detection of several wavelengths by fixed crystals and detectors. As many as 23 such wavelengths may be measured simultaneously with the most recent instruments.

the specimen pick up the several desired wavelengths simultaneously. Either flat or curved crystal geometry may be employed. Different types of crystals and detectors may be used on each channel for optimum detection over the wavelength range. Selective filters may also be used for the different channels. After a fixed time, the total intensity measured by each channel is printed out sequentially on a strip chart. Although the various channels may be readjusted as the elements to be detected change for different specimens, the advantage of rapid automatic measurement is largely lost if this must be done frequently.

Method B [12] is based on preselecting fixed position on a single spectrometer depending on the desired wavelengths; the spectrometer then automatically moves from one fixed position to the next without stopping in between. With this system, the number of elements that may be measured during each cycle is practically unlimited, but on the other hand, a particular crystal and detector may not be suitable for all of the elements desired. Each wavelength is measured at a different time so accurate control of the primary x-ray intensity or monitoring is required.

Each method has advantages and disadvantages. In Method A, the crystal, detectors, and filters may be chosen to be optimum for each separate wavelength, and a wide range of wavelengths may be covered. The number of elements that may be measured at one time is strictly limited physically by the amount of space around the x-ray tube. In Method B, there is only one detector circuit to maintain and it is easy to change the elements detected. It may not be possible, however, to reach all the wavelengths desired without changing the crystal and perhaps the detector. As is often the case, one method will be better suited to some industrial problems and the other method to other industrial problems.

Nondispersive Geometry

3.15. *Advantages and Limitations*

Previous sections in this chapter have dealt with various types of dispersing geometries. Because crystals are really rather inefficient in diffracting x-rays, more than 99.9 % of the energy is lost in the dispersing system. With the proportional and scintillation detectors to be described in Chapter 4, the amplitude of the electrical pulse coming from the detector is proportional to the energy of the x-ray quantum that caused it. Since the x-ray spectrum may be expressed in terms of energy as well as wavelength these detectors offer a rough means of separating the various x-ray spectral lines and make possible the elimination of the collimator and analyzing crystal for certain applications. Then the primary x-ray tube, specimen, and detector may be placed in close proximity as shown in Fig. 3-11. All the fluorescent radiation emitted by the specimen strikes the detector, and pulse amplitudes corresponding to all the energies (wavelengths) present will be generated. After the initial stages of amplification, the heterogeneous pulse amplitudes are fed into discriminating circuits. These circuits may be set to pass only a narrow range of pulse amplitudes and thus to pick out a correspondingly small energy range of the fluorescent x-ray spectrum. Unfortunately, as will be discussed further in Chapter 4, there is a spread of pulse amplitudes for each energy, and the resolution of neighboring x-ray lines is not complete. In fact, there is only partial resolution of elements two or three atomic numbers apart even under the best conditions, and there is never

complete enough resolution so that low concentrations of about
1 % of an element may be observed accurately. There are some
applications where the nondispersive system is very satisfactory

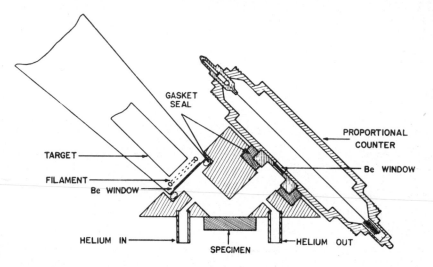

Fig. 3-11. Nondispersive x-ray optics. All of the radiation scattered and
emitted by the specimen can reach the detector. The x-ray spectrum is
distinguished by the energy of the lines through the use of pulse amplitude
analysis with proportional or scintillation detectors.

however. Measurement of tin plate on steel, to be discussed in
Chapter 6, is one example. The Sn K_α line is sufficiently separated
from the Fe K_α line that nondispersive optics give a good measure
of the tin thickness. Filters may also be used with or without nondispersive systems to remove particular radiations. For example
in brass, a nickel filter will selectively remove the Zn K_α radiation
but pass the Cu K_α radiation. Lowering the primary tube voltage
beyond the cut-off point for higher atomic number elements will
prevent their generation and so make possible the measurement
of lower atomic number elements without interference; an example
is the measurement of hafnium in the presence of zirconium.

For all of the analyzing systems, both dispersive and nondispersive, the same wavelength limitations exist on excitation and
detection of elements. That is, for elements of atomic number

lower than 22 (Ti), the wavelengths are strongly attenuated by air and it is therefore necessary to use a helium or hydrogen atmosphere or a vacuum throughout the analyzing system.

References

1. C. W. Bunn, *Chemical Crystallography*, Oxford Univ., London, 1946, p. 208.
2. R. Renninger, *Acta Cryst.* **7**, 677 (1954).
3. J. E. White, *J. Appl. Phys.* **21**, 885 (1950).
4. L. S. Birks and R. T. Seal, *J. Appl. Phys.* **28**, 541 (1957).
5. T. Johansson, *Naturwiss.*, **20**, 758 (1932).
6. L. S. Birks and E. J. Brooks, *Rev. Sci. Instr.* **24**, 992 (1953).
7a. L. S. Birks and E. J. Brooks, *Anal. Chem.* **27**, 437 (1955).
7b. J. W. Kemp, M. F. Hasler, J. L. Jones, and L. Zeitz, *Spectrochim. Acta* **7**, 141 (1955).
8. I. Adler and J. M. Axelrod, *Econ. Geol.*, **52**, 694 (1957).
9. G. Hägg and N. Karlsson, *Acta Cryst.* **5**, 728 (1952).
10. B. E. Warren, *J. Appl. Phys.* **25**, 814 (1954).
11. L. S. Birks and E. J. Brooks, *Anal. Chem.* **27**, 1147 (1955).
12. *Norelco Rep.* **1**, 127 (1954).

CHAPTER 4

DETECTION AND MEASUREMENT

Detectors

4.1. *Types of Detectors*

The detectors in common usage for x-ray spectrochemical analysis are the Geiger, proportional, and scintillation counters. Each has advantages and disadvantages as will be discussed below. Ionization chambers and photographic film are of limited usefulness and will not be considered here although mention was made of the use of film in the edge-crystal spectrograph described in Chapter 3. The three present detectors all operate on the principle of electronic amplification of the energy pulse generated when an x-ray quantum is absorbed. In this way, signals strong enough to operate scaling or integrating circuits are obtained. In Geiger counters, the pulse generated by an x-ray quantum is independent of the quantum energy, but in proportional or scintillation counters, each pulse amplitude is proportional to the corresponding x-ray quantum energy. Thus with the latter, a rough means is available to distinguish one element from another. More will be said about this in Sec. 4.4 on pulse amplitude discrimination.

To describe the basic physics underlying the processes which occur in the detectors is beyond the scope of this book and is not necessary for the x-ray analyst. Therefore, only a token explanation of the differences between the detectors and their method of operation will be given.

4.2. *The Geiger Counter and its Operation*

The Geiger counter requires least in the way of electronics and controls and is the simplest to use. Fig. 4-1 shows the common design of a Geiger tube. A cylindrical metal shell, A, has a thin mica or beryllium window, B, at one end. The other end is sealed by an insulator through which runs the central wire, W. The tube is filled with the "counting gas; a typical filling is argon at 0.5 to 0.7 atmospheres pressure and with a fraction of one per cent of

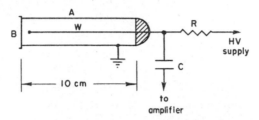

Fig. 4-1. The Geiger counter detector. Positive potential of 1 to 2 kev is applied to the central wire, W, through the resistor, R. A pulse caused by the absorption of an x-ray quantum is transmitted through the capacitor, C, to amplifying circuits. The metal shell, A, is grounded. B is the thin window of mica, Mylar, or other suitable material.

bromine or chlorine. Krypton or xenon may be substituted for the argon if wavelengths shorter than, say 1 A are to be detected. The noble gas acts to absorb x-rays and release electrons by ionization; the bromine or chlorine quenches the discharge, as explained below. The Geiger region is shown in Fig. 4-2. When the positive

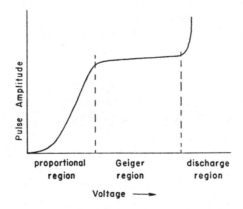

Fig. 4-2. The pulse amplitude in a tube such as shown in Fig. 4-1 increases with voltage on the central wire until a threshold is reached at the beginning of the Geiger region. There is very little change in pulse amplitude as the voltage is increased further until the discharge or corona region is reached.

potential applied to the wire of the tube is within the range indicated, the amplitude of the electrical pulse generated when an x-ray quantum is absorbed attains a fixed value and is independent of the quantum energy or of small variations in the Geiger tube voltage. This voltage region is known as the plateau of the counter. It usually extends over 100 to 200 volts and starts at a threshold of 500 to 1000 volts depending on the tube filling. The operation of the Geiger counter may be explained as follows.

Nothing happens until an x-ray quantum enters the window of the tube and ionizes an atom of the noble gas. Then the strong electric field accelerates the electron towards the central wire. This accelerating electron soon gains enough energy to ionize another atom and each electron ionizes more atoms, and so on until a small discharge called a Townsend avalanche builds up in the region of the initial ionization. At the same time, other discharges are built up along the whole length of the wire by the action of ultraviolet photons generated. Finally, there are avalanches of electrons striking the central wire all along the counter; 10^7 electrons may strike the wire in the order of 100 microseconds. The discharge process is halted by the sheath of positive ions moving out from the wire and lowering the effective electric field near the wire. The purpose of the "quenching" gas is to prevent reinitiation of the discharge when the positive ions strike the shell wall. The great number of electrons striking the wire momentarily lowers the tube voltage because the resistor, R, of Fig. 4-1 does not allow them to drain off; rather, the drop of voltage is passed as a pulse of a few millivolts by the capacitor, C. Amplifier circuits following the capacitor build up the pulse to values of the order of 50 volts. These pulses are then strong enough to operate scaling or integrating circuits.

The voltage on the wire is high enough so that any single ionization in the Geiger tube spreads quickly throughout the counter and builds up a discharge of about the same size each time before it is quenched. Thus the initial energy of the x-ray quantum is unimportant. During the time the discharge is building up and until it is quenched, the counter will not respond to new quanta entering the tube—that is, it is "dead." Dead time for Geiger counters is of the order of 100-200 microseconds and is far longer than for proportional or scintillation counters. Because of the dead time, the number of quanta per second that may be detected is limited; for a 200 microsecond dead time, the theoretical counting rate would be $1/(200 \times 10^{-6}) = 5000$ cps. In practice, the maximum number is actually somewhat higher than this, but there are appreciable losses even at 10 % of the maximum rate. A convenient rule of thumb is that 10 % loss occurs at 10 % of the maximum counting rate; for a maximum rate of 5000 cps, 50 counts would be lost at a counting rate of 500 cps. For quantitative analysis, it is necessary to stay below the 1 % loss level or to correct measured rates for losses. Correction is accomplished with a linearity curve as shown in Fig. 4-3. It is constructed by plotting the log of the measured intensity against the number of filters, where the filter factor or absorption for each thickness is known. Nickel or aluminum foils about 0.001 inches thick make suitable filters for plotting such a curve. By extrapolating the straight line portion, the true counting rate is obtained from the measured rate by moving vertically along the line AA' in the figure. Such a linearity curve, once plotted, will usually be valid for months of operation but may be checked quickly at any time by repeating the procedure with the filters.

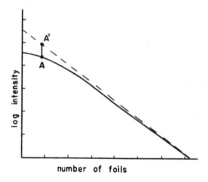

Fig. 4-3. Correction of Geiger counter data for nonlinearity of response. The log of the measured intensity is plotted vs. the number of layers of some absorber such as nickel or aluminum. Corrected intensity is obtained by extrapolating from some position A on the measured curve to position A' on the straight line that passes through the low intensity portion of the curve.

4.3. *The Gas Proportional Counter*

The gas proportional counter is often similar to the Geiger counter in construction and filling. Its important features are: (*1*) each
pulse from the counter is proportional in amplitude to the energy
of the x-ray quantum absorbed, and (*2*) the dead time is reduced
to the order of 0.2 microseconds. Hence the usable counting region
is increased to the order of 10^6 cps. Two common designs for gas
proportional counters are shown in Fig. 4-4. The top drawing is

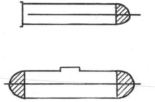

Fig. 4-4. The gas proportional counter may be either of the end window or
the side window type. The side window type will have a narrower distribution of pulse amplitudes. A second window may be placed on the back of the
side window tube so that x-radiation that is not absorbed may escape from
the tube and not cause q-high background.

the same as the Geiger counter and, in fact, it is often possible to
use a Geiger counter as a proportional counter by dropping the
high voltage to the proportional region shown in Fig. 4-2. However,
with a side window design as in the bottom drawing of Fig. 4-4,
the output pulses will show a minimum amplitude spread for
monochromatic x-rays, and this is considered the preferred design.
With side-window detectors, the path length is greatly reduced and
it is necessary to use a heavy filling gas such as xenon to absorb the
x-rays. The action in a proportional counter is somewhat different
than in a Geiger counter. In a Geiger counter, the operating voltage
is so high that each ionization builds up to the maximum discharge
permitted by the positive ion sheath that forms around the wire.
With the lower voltage used on a proportional counter, the ionization does not spread along the wire and the size of the output pulse
is proportional to the number of initial ionizations caused by a
particular x-ray quantum. The number of initial ionizations de-

pends on the quantum energy in the following way. For example, the Cu K_α quantum has an energy of 8020 volts and the ionization potential of xenon is 12.08 volts. Therefore, each Cu K_α quantum should cause 665 initial ionizations. For Ag K_α on the other hand, the quantum energy is 22100 volts and should cause 1830 initial ionizations. Thus the output pulse amplitude for Ag K_α should be about 2.8 times the pulse amplitude from Cu K_α. This then is the proportional action from which the counter gets its name. Because the discharge does not spread all along the wire as in the Geiger counter, most of the tube volume remains active rather than dead during the buildup from one quantum, and thus a successive quantum may also cause a pulse. The dead time is only the collection time for the avalanches from one quantum and may be of the order of 0.2 microseconds. The maximum counting rate is increased by two or three orders of magnitude over the Geiger counter, and the working level is usually 10,000 cps or greater.

4.4. Pulse Height Analysis

Although the number of initial ionizations was given as 665 for Cu K_α and 1830 for Ag K_α, these are only average values; actually the output pulse amplitude shows a Gaussian distribution due to statistical fluctuations. The situation is illustrated in Fig. 4-5a and b. In Fig. 4-5a, the energy of the Cu and Ag x-ray quanta are properly shown as monoenergetic lines. The corresponding output

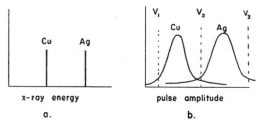

x-ray energy   pulse amplitude

a.   b.

Fig. 4-5. In a proportional counter, the copper and silver lines of the left hand drawing will each lead to a distribution of pulse amplitudes as shown in the right hand drawing By electronically accepting only pulse amplitudes between V_1 and V_2, the copper radiation will be measured but most of the silver radiation will be rejected. Conversely, by accepting pulses between V_2 and V_3, the silver will be measured and the copper rejected.

pulse distributions from the proportional counter are shown in Fig. 4-5b. The standard deviation σ for each curve is just $\sqrt{n_i}$, where n_i is the calculated number of initial ionizations. That is, $\sigma_{Cu} = 25.8$ ionizations, and $\sigma_{Ag} = 42.8$ ionizations. After suitable amplification, the pulses may be put through a pulse height analyzer circuit * that passes only pulses of amplitude between say V_2 and V_3 in Fig. 4-5b. Almost all of the Ag K_α pulses will be counted but very few of the Cu K_α pulses—only those in the tail of the Cu K_α distribution that extends above V_2. If the analyzer is set to accept pulses between V_1 and V_2, then the situation will be reversed and most of the Cu K_α pulses will be counted but very few of the Ag K_α pulses will be counted. The spread of the pulse amplitude distribution is determined by statistics and is such that neighboring elements may not be resolved by pulse amplitude discrimination alone.** Hendee and Fine [2] showed that the overlap was approximately constant independent of atomic number. Resolution of elements separated by 2 or 3 atomic numbers is feasible if the concentrations are say 10 % or greater. Concentrations lower than 1 % are usually not distinguishable above the tails of the

---

* A highly simplified picture of the operation of a pulse height analyzer is as follows: First the pulses are all amplified to bring them up to usable value but keeping the same relative distribution of amplitudes. Then a minimum amplitude is selected and an electronic circuit (discriminator) is set so that amplitudes below this will not pass. Next, a maximum amplitude is selected and a second electronic circuit is set to pass only pulses of this amplitude or greater. In operation, if the pulse is below the minimum, it will not pass the first circuit and will be lost. If it is between the minimum and maximum amplitudes it will pass only the first circuit and will go on to the recorder. If it is above the maximum amplitude, it will pass both the first and second circuits thus generating two simultaneous pulses; an anti-coincidence cancels these two so that nothing reaches the recorder. For a comprehensive explanation of the pulse height analyzer, the reader is referred to W. C. Elmore and M. Sands, *Electronics Experimental Techniques*, McGraw-Hill, New York, 1949; and also to J. E. Francis, P. R. Bell, and J. C. Gundlach, *Rev. Sci. Instr.* **22**, 133 (1951).

** It has been observed by some workers that resolution of neighboring elements at about atomic number 13 (Al) is possible theoretically because the K_α and K_β lines both occur within the statistical spread of one of the lines. Thus the overlap of adjacent elements is relatively less than for elements in the neighborhood of Fe (26).

distributions from the major constituents no matter what the separation of the elements in atomic number.

4.5. *Escape Peak: its Cause and Possible Use*

There is a phenomenon in proportional counters known as the escape peak.[1] When the energy of the entering x-ray quantum is high enough, it may knock out one of the K electrons in the noble gas rather than just ionize the atoms. When this happens, a K series x-ray quantum of the noble gas is emitted, and, because the gas is quite transparent to its own radiation, this emitted x-ray quantum usually escapes from the detector. The energy of the emitted x-ray quantum must be subtracted from that of the original x-ray quantum and thus the amplitude of that particular pulse is reduced. Under favorable conditions, a large fraction of the pulses generated in the detector arise from such a process and cause the escape peak shown in Fig. 4-6 for a krypton-filled detector and

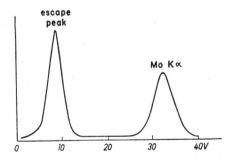

Fig. 4-6. The escape peak on the left is generated when Mo K_α radiation, represented by the right hand peak, is absorbed in a krypton filled proportional counter. The two peaks have a separation related to the energy of the Kr K_α x-ray energy.

Mo K_α radiation. The escape peak is less common in xenon-filled detectors because the initial x-ray quantum must have an energy greater than 34 kv to knock out one of the K electrons. This only occurs for the K series x-rays from elements of atomic number greater than 59 (Pr).

When the escape peak is strong it may be used for practical measurements [1] as follows. For neighboring elements, the main pulse amplitude distributions will overlap. The escape peaks are separated by the same number of volts as in the main peaks, but the absolute line breadths are smaller because they correspond to a smaller number of events as discussed in Sec. 4.4. Therefore the relative separation is greater and the resolution is better. Most of the time, however, the presence of escape peaks only interferes with the measurements, and the counter filling should be chosen to avoid them.

4.6. *The Scintillation Counter*

The scintillation counter consists of material such as a thallium-activated sodium-iodide crystal block and a photomultiplier. X-ray quanta absorption in the crystal block causes pulses of visible light to be emitted by the crystal atoms and detected by the photo-multiplier. The number of light pulses generated depends on the energy of the x-ray quantum and so this type of detector is also a proportional counter. As with the gas proportional counter, the dead time is very short and high counting rates may be employed. The number of visible light photons emitted for absorption of one x-ray quantum is greater than the number of ionizations for gas proportional counters, but less than 10 % of the light photons reaching the photomultiplier cause emission of an electron from the photo-surface. Thus the number of electrons generated in the photomultiplier for a given x-ray quantum energy is actually less than the number of ionizations in a gas proportional counter. The whole pulse amplitude spectrum is shifted to lower values and the output pulse distributions from scintillation counters are relatively broader than those from proportional counters (2 to 3 times as broad). Consequently, there is more overlap of neighboring wavelengths and poorer resolution of elements with scintillation counters. Escape peak phenomena are possible in scintillation counters just as in gas proportional counters but the elements in the scintillation crystal will require different energies to knock out the K electrons than did the krypton or xenon of the gas proportional counters.

Although it might be thought that the numerous spurious pulses generated in the photomultiplier tube itself would interfere with detection of the characteristic pulses, this is usually not the case. These spurious pulses occur over a relatively narrow range at the zero amplitude end of the scale and are eliminated with even the simplest pulse height discriminator circuits. However, when scintillation crystals are used to detect long wavelength radiation, the low pulse amplitudes may approach those of the spurious noise pulses, and this, in fact, is one way in which the suitable wavelength range is limited for scintillation detectors.

4.7. Relative Merits of the Three Types of Detectors

To evaluate the merits of the three types of detectors, several factors must be considered.

Circuitry required. The Geiger counter requires far less circuitry than either the proportional or scintillation detectors. Because of the 100-200 volt operating plateau, the voltage supply for the Geiger counter need not be well regulated. The pulses from the Geiger counter are of the order of millivolts as compared with microvolts for the proportional or scintillation detector. Thus, fewer stages of amplification are required with Geiger counters.

Counting rates. Useable counting rates with proportional or scintillation detectors are of the order of 10,000 cps or higher as compared with 1,000 cps or less for Geiger counters. Thus they are more suitable for automatic semi-quantitative scanning of a complete spectrum where both strong and weak lines occur.

Pulse amplitude. Pulse amplitude with proportional and scintillation detectors is proportional to the energy of the x-ray quantum. The distribution of amplitudes is 2-3 times as broad with scintillation counters as with proportional counters; thus resolution of neighboring wavelengths is poorer with the scintillation counters. Pulse amplitude discrimination circuits are not conveniently adapted to automatic scanning of spectra because the pulse amplitudes for the various elements are not linearly related to the Bragg angles for the same elements, and so the voltage accepted by the discrimination circuit would have to be constantly adjusted in a nonlinear fashion with change in angle. In Geiger counters, the pulse amplitude is independent of x-ray energy.

Wavelength sensitivity. Sensitivity of Geiger and proportional counters depends on the absorption of the gas filling. In general, both these detectors are most sensitive around the range of 0.5 to 3 A. By using a thin Mylar window and flowing the counting gas through the detector continuously, the sensitivity is extended down towards 10 A. Scintillation detectors have almost 100 % theoretical sensitivity for all the x-ray wavelengths. For the range from say 2 A and shorter they attain almost their theoretical sensitivity. For the longer wavelengths they are limited because of the hygroscopic nature of NaI which is the most common crystal presently used. In order to protect the crystal from moisture, it is necessary to coat it with a layer that usually absorbs more soft x-rays than the windows of the gas filled detectors. As the operating voltage on x-ray tubes is increased to 100 kev and the shorter x-rays are generated, the scintillation counter will become more important because the gas filled detectors have very poor sensitivity below 0.5 A.

Monitors

4.8.   *Reasons for Using a Monitor and Method of Operation*

Although the electronic detectors measure the intensity reaching them with any desired statistical accuracy, there must be some assurance that the overall x-ray intensity is not varying with time when quantitative analysis is attempted. If there are variations with time, some means of correcting or overcoming them must be achieved. Systems for controlling or correcting the x-ray intensity may be either simple or elaborate depending on the accuracy required. Line voltage stabilizers ahead of the x-ray power supply and current stabilizers in the x-ray tube circuit help control the output of primary x-rays and result in stability suitable for most quantitative analysis provided comparison measurements are made on standards several times a day. For very accurate measurements, it is sometimes necessary, however, to monitor the x-rays leaving the specimen and in special cases to monitor just the particular wavelength of interest.

To monitor the x-rays from the specimen, an electronic detector similar to the Geiger, proportional, or scintillation counters described above may be used. It should be fixed in position, preferably near the analyzer crystal location so it will receive similar radiation to that being analyzed. There is one important consideration in the monitor operation that should not be overlooked. *It should be adjusted to operate at as high a counting rate as is feasible and may even be beyond the linear response region.* This is so it will introduce minimum statistical error into the measurements. Since the use of a monitor is of interest only in quantitative analysis, the condition of operation will not be continuous scanning of the spectrum but rather fixed total count or fixed total time operation at a particular wavelength setting of the spectrometer. The monitor circuit may be operated simultaneously with the measuring detector and the variations in monitor readings used to correct the measurements, or the monitor may be set to record a fixed total count and when this has been obtained, to cut off the measuring detector circuit. In the latter arrangement, the measuring detector reading is automatically corrected for variations in the x-ray output and differences in readings are due only to changes in composition of the specimen. A slightly more elaborate but better means of monitoring the x-ray output from the primary x-ray tube is to use a separate specimen for the monitor. For instance, to one side of the regular specimen, a small additional specimen of chosen composition may be placed and shielded so that fluorescent radiation from it will reach only the monitor. Usually the monitor will read all the fluorescent radiation from the additional specimen, but in instances where the x-ray tube operating voltage is very critical, a crystal or filter may be used ahead of the monitor so that only one wavelength will be monitored.

Statistics

4.9.   *Type of Statistics for x-Ray Measurements*

The time distribution of emitted x-rays obeys the same random time distribution as radioactive decay, and the statistical errors involved in measuring such distributions are well understood. When a detector such as a Geiger counter has measured a total of

N quanta, the expected standard deviation, σ_{exp} is just $\sqrt{N}$. This σ_{exp} should be compared with the observed standard deviation, σ_{obs}, in ordinary statistics. For ordinary measurements, an observation is repeated n times; x_i is the value obtained for a single observation; μ is the average of all x_i. Then σ_{obs} is obtained from the equation

$$\sigma_{obs} = [\sum (x_i - \mu)^2 / (n-1)]^{\frac{1}{2}} \qquad (4\text{-}1)$$

By repeating an x-ray measurement n times, σ_{obs} may be found and compared with σ_{exp} calculated from any one of the measurements. Table 4-1 shows a set of 10 measurements on the $Zn\,K_\alpha$

TABLE 4-1

Variability in Repeated Measurements on the $Z_n\,K_\alpha$ Line at a Total Count of 10,000 for each Measurement

Counting time, secs	Dev. from av	Dev.²
160	0.4	0.16
159	0.6	0.36
163	3.4	11.56
160	0.4	0.16
160	0.4	0.16
157	2.6	6.76
160	0.4	0.16
160	0.4	0.16
159	0.6	0.36
158	1.6	2.56
Sum 1596		22.40
Av 159.6		

line in a powder specimen. The average value μ for the time required to accumulate 10,000 counts is 159.6 seconds; the sum, $\sum$, of terms $(x_i - \mu)^2$ is 22.4; $n-1 = 9$; σ_{obs} is found to be 1.57. Returning to σ_{exp} from detector statistics, we may take any one of the measurements such as the fifth one where $x_i = 160$ seconds. For each x_i the total number of pulses, N, counted is 10,000 and $\sigma_{exp} = \sqrt{10000} = 100$ pulses. This must be converted to seconds for comparison with the σ_{obs} above. At the value of x_i chosen, the 10,000 counts were accumulated in 160 seconds. Therefore

$\sigma_{\text{exp}} = 100$ pulses corresponds to 1.6 seconds. The two values of $\sigma_{\text{obs}} = 1.57$ seconds and $\sigma_{\text{exp}} = 1.6$ seconds, agree very well as is usually the case when N is between 10^4 and 10^5 counts. For N greater than 10^5, σ_{obs} will often be larger than σ_{exp} because other errors enter into the measurements due to instrumental or experimental variations.

A more meaningful term than standard deviation is coefficient of variation which is standard deviation expressed in percent of the measured value; for convenience it may be written as $\sigma \%$. For a total of N counts,

$$\sigma \% = 100\sigma_{\text{exp}}/N = 100\sqrt{N}/N = 100/\sqrt{N}.$$

Thus when an x-ray line has been measured long enough to yield a total of 10,000 counts the composition of that element is said to have a precision of 1 % of the amount present. Some workers prefer to use confidence levels rather standard deviation. It is easy to convert from one to the other; 1σ represents 67 % confidence, 2σ represents 95 % confidence, and 3σ represents 99 % confidence. That is, if $\sigma \%$ for a given measurement is 1 % of the amount present, we are 67 % sure that the answer obtained is really within 1 % of the correct answer, 95 % sure that it is within 2 % of the correct answer, and 99 % sure that it is within 3 % of the correct answer.

4.10.   Taking Account of Background Intensity

In x-ray measurements, the characteristic lines always appear above a background value. If the background value amounts to say 5 % of the line peak, it is necessary to consider it in calculating the expected standard deviation of the line measurement. Let N_l be the total counts measured at the line peak and N_b be the total counts measured at the background position in the same length of time. The coefficient of variation for the line is then calculated from the equation

$$\sigma \% = (N_l + N_b)^{\frac{1}{2}}/(N_l - N_b) \tag{4-2}$$

A detailed consideration of the mathematically optimum division of counting time for peak and background, in order to satisfy predetermined values of standard deviation, may be found in a paper by Mack and Spielberg.[3]

4.11. *Effect on Precision when a Monitor is Used*

When a monitor is used, the detector statistics must be revised to include the error introduced by the monitor. The same type of statistics apply for the monitor, and if the monitor count is N_m, its standard deviation is $\sqrt{N_m}$. First consider the situation when the background is negligible. Suppose that during the same time interval required for the monitor to receive its N_m counts, the detector receives N_l counts. The standard deviation for the monitor is $\sqrt{N_m}$ and for the detector is $\sqrt{N_l}$. The monitor standard deviation restated in terms of detector counts is $(\sqrt{N_m}/N_m) \times N_l$, and now the two contributing standard deviations for the detector may be combined by the usual rule for adding variances. That is:

$$\sigma_l = (N_l + N_l^2/N_m)^{\frac{1}{2}} = [N_l(1+N_l/N_m)]^{\frac{1}{2}} \doteq N_l^{\frac{1}{2}} \times (1+N_l/N_m)^{\frac{1}{2}}. \quad (4\text{-}3)$$

It is easily seen from this that if the monitor is counting much faster than the detector, then N_l/N_m is a small fraction and does not contribute much to the error. It may be stated approximately that a monitor will improve accuracy only if N_l/N_m is less than twice the variation in the x-ray output that the monitor is supposed to correct. For example, suppose the x-ray output varies by 5 %; if the value of N_l/N_m is 10 %, then the standard deviation of the line is $\sqrt{N_l} \times \sqrt{1.1} = 1.05 N_l$ from Eq. 4-4. But this is an increase of 5 % over the value without the monitor and no improvement has been achieved.

When the background must be considered, a term for the monitor's contribution to background error must be added. It is N_b^2/N_m corresponding to the term N_l^2/N_m for the monitor's contribution to the line. Eq. 4-2 then becomes:

$$\sigma\% = [N_l + N_b + (N_l^2 + N_b^2)/N_m]^{\frac{1}{2}}/(N_l - N_b). \quad (4\text{-}4)$$

Practical Limit of Detectability

4.12. *Line Intensity above the 3σ Value for Background*

The statistics of the preceding paragraphs apply in a mathematical sense no matter how weak the x-ray line to be detected. However, there is some reasonable limit on what is detectable in

practice. Several acceptable definitions might be made but perhaps
the most satisfactory one is that the line must be above the background by at least 3 standard deviations of the background. Fig. 4-7
illustrates the situation. Suppose the background level is 100
counts; then $\sigma = 10$ counts and $3\sigma = 30$ counts. The dotted lines
in Fig. 4-7 mark the 3σ limits and the background will remain

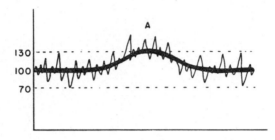

Fig. 4-7. The minimum composition detectable by x-rays may be defined
as that concentration that yields an intensity equal to three standard
deviations of the background intensity. When the heavy curve is drawn
through the average intensity variations, it is seen to reach the 3σ bound
at position A and the composition corresponding to position A would be
just detectable according to the definition.

within these bounds 99 % of the time. The heavy solid line is the
average line and rises to the 3σ bound at position A. This line
would be just detectable according to the definition. Let us examine the coefficient of variation for the line measurement using
Eq. 4-2. Substituting 130 for N_l and 100 for N_b, σ % is found to be
$15.2/30 = 50$ %. If from a previously known calibration curve,
the value of 30 counts above background represents say 0.01 %
composition, then 0.01 % is the minimum composition detectable
and the precision of the measurement is 50 % of the amount
present or 0.005 %.

   The advantage of the above definition for the lower detectable
limit is that it gives about 50 % for the coefficient of variation over
a wide range of total counts or counting rates. For instance, if the
example above were changed so that $N_b = 10,000$ counts, then
$\sigma_b = 100$; $3\sigma_b = 300$; $N_l = 10,300$ counts and σ % $= 143/300 =$
48 %.

References

1. P. H. Dowling, C. F. Hendee, T. R. Kohler, and W. Parrish, *Norelco Reptr.* **4**, 23 (1957).
2. C. F. Hendee and S. Fine; *Phys. Rev.* **95**, 281 (1954).

CHAPTER 5

TECHNIQUES FOR QUANTITATIVE ANALYSIS

5.1. *Variation of Intensity versus Composition in General*

Previous chapters have described techniques for generating the characteristic x-ray spectra in a specimen and for measuring the intensity of the spectral lines. For quantitative analysis, it is necessary to relate the measured intensity of each line to the proper value of percent composition in the particular specimen. Although the relation between intensity and composition is more nearly linear in x-ray spectroscopy than in emission spectroscopy, it is not sufficiently linear for direct quantitative analysis. Relative intensities of the different lines in the spectrum from a specimen will, of course, be dependent on the factors discussed in the earlier chapters, i.e., x-ray tube voltage, spectrometer geometry, choice of analyzing crystal, detector statistics, etc. All of these things could be held more or less constant, however, and proper relations established easily. More important for consideration here, and in fact, the controlling or limiting factor in all practical quantitative analysis is the "matrix effect" that varies for each composition and must be corrected either by computation or the use of calibration standards or a combination of both. The matrix effect as used here includes both absorption and enhancement. The absorption comes about because characteristic x-rays are generated below as well as at the surface of the specimen, and both the primary and characteristic x-rays must pass through increasing amounts of matrix material as one goes deeper into the specimen. The well-known equation for loss of intensity by absorption for a particular wavelength, λ, is

$$I_\lambda = I_0 \exp\left(-\mu\rho x\right)$$

for a path length, x, density ρ, and mass absorption coefficient μ; I_0 is the incident intensity and I_λ is the transmitted intensity.

Enhancement occurs when the characteristic fluorescent lines from some of the matrix elements act to excite the characteristic spectrum of the desired element. It is not easy to write an equation for the enhancement effect, but the magnitude of the effect depends on matrix composition, primary and secondary wave length, etc. In computing expected intensities, both absorption and enhancement must be considered as will be shown in the following section.

Quantitative Analysis by Computation

5.2.   Derivation of a General Family of Equations for Expected Fluorescent Intensity

Derivation of the equations will follow the general method used by Hamos.[1] Consider Fig. 5-1. Primary radiation strikes the specimen at angle ϕ_1 and fluorescent radiation emerges at angle ϕ_2. We will consider first a single wavelength, λ, in the primary beam.

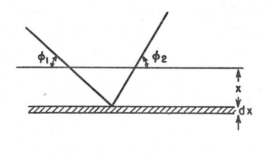

Fig. 5-1. Excitation of characteristic radiation in a layer dx at a distance x below the specimen surface. Primary radiation strikes the surface at angle ϕ_1 and fluorescent radiation emerges at angle ϕ_2.

Its intensity is given by $I_{0\lambda}$. The matrix will have an effective absorption coefficient μ for this wavelength. According to the standard absorption equation, the intensity reaching the layer dx will be

$$I_{1\lambda} = I_0 \exp\left(-\mu\rho x \csc \phi_1\right) \qquad (5\text{-}1)$$

where ρ is the density of the specimen. This radiation will cause fluorescence of the characteristic radiation of the element i in the layer dx. The amount of characteristic radiation generated will be

$$dI_{1i} = Q_i \rho_i I_{1\lambda} \, dx \tag{5-2}$$

where Q_i is an excitation constant and ρ_i is the density of element i in the layer dx. This radiation must pass back out of the specimen and the absorption coefficient of the matrix will be μ'. The intensity reaching the surface will be

$$dI_{2i} = dI_{1i} \exp\left(-\mu' \rho x \csc \phi_2\right). \tag{5-3}$$

Substituting from Eqs. 5-1 and 5-2, we obtain

$$dI_{2i} = \{Q_i \rho_i I_{0\lambda} \exp\left[-(\mu \csc \phi_1 + \mu' \csc \phi_2)\rho x\right]\} \, dx. \tag{5-4}$$

In practice, ϕ_1 and ϕ_2 will be held constant, and since μ and μ' are also constant for a given specimen, the terms in parentheses in Eq. 5-4 may be replaced by a single constant μ''; the exponent becomes simply $-\mu'' \rho x$. Integrating Eq. 5-4 from zero to x with substitution we obtain

$$I_{2i} = \frac{Q_i \rho_i I_{0\lambda}}{\mu'' \rho} \left[1 - \exp\left(-\mu'' \rho x\right)\right]. \tag{5-5}$$

As x is allowed to go to infinity, Eq. 5-5 becomes simply

$$I_{2i} = Q_i \rho_i I_{0\lambda} / \mu'' \rho. \tag{5-6}$$

Similar equations will result for each wavelength in the primary beam but with different values for μ''. It is not easy to prove rigorously that μ'' may include enhancement as well as absorption coefficients, but it can be imagined intuitively and was verified experimentally by Beattie and Brissey.[2] The term ρ may now be expressed in terms of the densities of the individual components of the matrix. Also, μ'' may be expressed in terms of new coefficients a_{ij} representing the overall effect of element j on element i and taking into account all the wavelengths that will excite element i. The term $\mu'' \rho$ then becomes

$$\mu'' \rho = a_{i1} \rho_1 + a_{i2} \rho_2 + \ldots + a_{ii} \rho_i + \ldots + a_{in} \rho_n \tag{5-7}$$

Eq. 5-6 may now be rewritten as

$$a_{i1} \rho_1 + a_{i2} \rho_2 + \ldots + a_{ii} \rho_i + \ldots + a_{in} \rho_n = Q_i \rho_i I_0 / I_i \tag{5-8}$$

where the subscripts λ have been dropped out because all wavelengths are included. Unfortunately, the terms a_{ij} are not really constants but themselves are functions of all the other ρ's. Sherman [3] has examined this complex relation in detail, but the resulting equations usually cannot be solved exactly except for systems of a few components. There are situations, however, when the a_{ij} may be considered constant to a first or second order approximation. The term a_{ii} is always a constant and in fact is equal to unity. This may be shown by solving Eq. 5-8 for the case of pure element i; all the ρ's are equal to zero except ρ_i and it is equal to the total density ρ. The intensity I_i takes the value of the pure element I_{pi} and Eq. 5-8 becomes

$$a_{ii}\rho = Q_i\rho I_0/I_{pi} \tag{5-9}$$

The ρ's drop out and it is recalled that Q_i is just the constant relating the incident primary intensity to the emitted intensity; in other words, $Q_i I_0 \equiv I_{pi}$, and Eq. 5-9 reduces to $a_{ii} = 1$. Eq. 5-8 may be rewritten by substituting the above values for $Q_i I_0$ and a_{ii} and gathering terms.

$$a_{i1}\rho_1 + a_{i2}\rho_2 + \ldots + (1-I_{pi}/I_i)\rho_i + \ldots + a_{in}\rho_n = 0 \tag{5-10}$$

In fact, similar equations may be written for each component in the specimen and the family of equations becomes

$$
\begin{aligned}
(1-I_{p1}/I_1)W_1 + a_{12}W_2 + a_{13}W_3 + \ldots + a_{1n}W_n &= 0 \\
a_{21}W_1 + (1-I_{p2}/I_2)W_2 + a_{23}W_3 + \ldots + a_{2n}W_n &= 0 \\
\cdot\ \cdot\ \cdot\ \cdot\ \cdot\ \cdot\ \cdot\ \cdot\ \cdot\ \cdot\ \cdot\ \cdot\ \cdot\ \cdot\ \cdot \\
a_{n1}W_1 + a_{n2}W_2 + a_{n3}W_3 + \ldots + (1-I_{pn}/I_n)W_n &= 0
\end{aligned}
\tag{5-11}
$$

where we have divided through in Eq. 5-10 by the density of the specimen ρ so that ρ_i/ρ becomes the weight fraction W_i and

$$W_1 + W_2 + W_3 + \ldots + W_n = 1 \tag{5-12}$$

This is the same nomenclature used by Beattie and Brissey.[2]

5.3. Solution of a Family of Equations using a First Approximation

It is apparent that Eq. 5-11 cannot be solved unless the terms a_{ij} can all be evaluated. To a first approximation, each a_{ij} may be assumed to be dependent on elements i and j alone and its value found by measuring the intensities obtained from pure elements i and j and a binary mixture containing i and j in known amounts. This was the technique adopted by Beattie and Brissey,[2] and they obtained good agreement with wet chemical analysis on alloys of Cr-Fe-Ni-Mo. Their errors ranged from 0.5% to 6.5% of the amount present. As an example of the procedure, suppose we wish to find the term a_{37} in Eq. 5-11. First the intensity of pure element 3 is measured to give I_{p3}. Then a binary containing only elements 3 and 7 is prepared at about a 50-50 composition (if we should know the approximate relative composition of elements 3 and 7 in the unknown specimens, it is better to prepare the binary somewhere near that relative composition than at a 50-50 mixture). The third equation in the family 5-11 is chosen; all the terms drop out except those in W_3 and W_7 and we may write

$$(1-I_{p3}/I_3)W_3+a_{37}W_7 = 0$$

from which a_{37} becomes

$$a_{37} = (I_{p3}/I_3-1)/W_3/W_7 \tag{5-13}$$

Likewise, the seventh equation of 5-11 and the same standards allow us to solve for a_{73}, which is found to be

$$a_{73} = (I_{p7}/I_7-1)W_7/W_3$$

In general

$$a_{ij} = (I_{pi}/I_i-1)W_i/W_j \tag{5.14}$$

For a set of specimens containing, say, four elements in various amounts, it will be necessary to prepare ten standards: the four pure elements and the six binaries comprising all pairs of elements. Once this has been done and the a_{ij}'s found, it will be possible to calculate the composition for any specimen containing those four elements *to a first approximation.*

5.4. *Solution of a Family of Equations using a Second Approximation*

A better approximation in solving Eq. 5-11 for multicomponent systems is to solve for the a_{ij}'s from ternaries containing three of the elements in the specimens. Kemp and Andermann [4] calculated expected intensities for alloys of Fe-Cr-Ni-Mn-Mo using essentially this second order approximation although their starting equations were in somewhat different form then Eq. 5-11. Their agreement with wet chemistry was within a few tenths percent of the amount present. The simplest case in which this approximation is quite accurate is when one major component remains in the same percentage range from sample to sample, while the other components vary in any manner. This situation is often encountered in nickel-base high temperature alloys or iron-base stainless steels. To show the procedure, suppose all the specimens in a given system contain of the order of 65–70 % nickel. Nickel is then set up as element 1 in Eq. 5-11. Again suppose we are interested in the coefficients for elements 3 and 7. First we will find the coefficient a_{31} by using pure nickel, pure element 3 and a binary containing 70 % nickel and 30 % element 3.

$$a_{31} = (I_{p3}/I_3 - 1)W_3/W_1$$
$$a_{13} = (I_{p1}/I_1 - 1)W_1/W_3$$

Using a binary containing 70 % nickel and 30 % element 7, the coefficient a_{71} is obtained similarly.

$$a_{71} = (I_{p7}/I_7 - 1)W_7/W_1$$
$$a_{17} = (I_{p1}/I_1 - 1)W_1/W_7$$

We now prepare a ternary containing 70 % nickel with the balance about equally divided between elements 3 and 7. The third equation of the family 5-11 is now written

$$a_{31}W_1 + (I_{p3}/I_3 - 1)W_3 + a_{37}W_7 = 0$$

It may be solved for a_{37} because all of the other terms are known from the composition of the ternary and the measurements above. Likewise, the seventh equation of 5-11 becomes

$$a_{71}W_1 + a_{73}W_3 + (I_{p7}/I_7 - 1)W_7 = 0$$

and may be solved for a_{73}.

Thus each coefficient a_{ij} may be determined, and for a system of six elements, 21 standards are required: the six pure elements, the five binaries with 70 % nickel, and the ten ternaries each containing 70 % nickel plus pairs of the remaining five elements.

5.5. *When Computation Methods should be Used*

From the preceding section it is apparent that calculation of compositions is a lengthy process for a set of specimens. Once the coefficients have been found, however, they will always be valid for that particular system of elements, and the equations may be arranged for rapid solution. The calculation procedures have advantage only when the number of comparison standards that would otherwise be required is appreciably larger than the number of standards required to calculate the coefficients a_{ij}.

5.6. *A Special Situation for Specimens of Limited Quantity*

A special situation exists for specimens that are limited either in thickness or in total amount, for example, plating layers or residue from chemical extractions. Refering back to Sec. 5.2, Eq. 5-5, we may write for the intensity of element i in a layer of thickness t, the equation

$$I_i = [I_{pi}\rho_i/\textstyle\sum_j(a_{ij}\rho_j)]\{1-\exp[-(\textstyle\sum_j a_{ij}\rho_j)t]\} \qquad (5\text{-}15)$$

For layers where t is small, the exponential may be approximated by the first two terms of the series expansion $\exp(-y) \approx (1-y)$ giving

$$I_i = [I_{pi}\rho_i/\textstyle\sum(a_{ij}\rho_j)][1-1+(\textstyle\sum a_{ij}\rho_j)t]$$

and this reduces immediately to

$$I_i = I_{pi}\rho_i t \qquad (5\text{-}16)$$

Thus the intensity of each component in the system is linearly related to thickness and is not affected by the other components since the $\sum a_{ij}\rho_j$ dropped out. Without even knowing ρ_i, the measured intensity is simply related to the quantity of element i in grams per square cm. Eq. 5-16 applies equally well to all limited specimens whether they be in the form of thin films or not. Experimental verification of Eq. 5-16 was found by Rhodin[5] and others.

Quantitative Analysis by Comparison with Standards

5.7.   *Use of Analyzed Specimens as Standard*

Because of the lengthy preparatory work that must be done in order to make use of the computational methods in the preceding sections, many workers prefer to rely entirely on comparison with standards for quantitative analysis. In general the intensity versus composition relation for an element in a matrix is not a straight line but rather a curved line, as the ones in Fig. 5-2. Curve a, re-

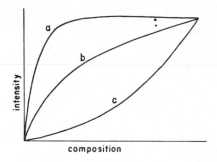

Fig. 5-2. Variation of the intensity vs. composition curve with matrix effect. Curve a, a heavy element in a light element matrix; in curve b, the absorption of the matrix is only slightly less than the self-absorption of the desired element; in curve c, the matrix absorption is slightly greater than the self-absorption of the desired element.

presents a heavy element in a light matrix. Because of the low matrix absorption, the intensity rises rapidly at first and then levels off toward the 100 % value. Curves b and c are the more common variety. In curve b, the absorption of the matrix is slightly less than the self-absorption of the desired element; in curve c, it is slightly greater than the self-absorption. The three curves of Fig. 5-2 may represent the family of calibration curves for one particular element in a range of matrix materials.

It is not always necessary to plot whole curves as in Fig. 5-2. Often standards of a few known compositions are used to give a short section of the curve, or just two standards are used to give two points and a straight line relation assumed between the two points. If Fig. 5-2 does represent a family of calibration curves for a particular element, then the matrix composition of the standards must be chosen to correspond to that of the unknown so that the proper curve may be used.

In practical work, the comparison with standards may be done in several ways depending on the nature of the specimen and the number of elements to be determined. In the steel industry for instance, the producer will have various alloys each with a limited range of composition. He wishes to know if a given heat meets the specifications. The simplest approach is to have an analyzed standard for each type of alloy and to compare the x-ray intensities from each element in a representative set of samples from the heat with the x-ray intensities from each element in the analyzed standard. A linear relationship for intensity versus composition between the standards and unknowns will usually suffice. That is, if 18 % chromium in the standard yields 15,000 cps, a measurement of 15,250 cps in the unknown means that it contains 18.3 % chromium. The standard deviation will depend on the total number of counts, but very careful work is required if the standard deviation is to be reduced to less than 0.2 % of the amount present no matter how high the total number of counts. In some cases, it will be advisable to have two analyzed standards representing the nominal limits of the desired alloy composition. Comparison standards and unknowns should, of course, be physically similar.

For other types of materials such as gasoline where the bromine or lead content may vary over a range of two or three times the average value, it will be better to draw a calibration curve from laboratory prepared standards and then to compare measured intensities with the calibration curve to obtain the composition. When two or more elements vary independently over a large range and are known to affect each other by absorption or enhancement, it may be necessary to prepare a family of calibration curves for several composition values of one of the elements.

5.8. *Use of Internal Standards*

In other types of specimens such as minerals, the elements of interest may occur in a variety of matrix materials. Comparison standards or calibration curves would be required for each type of matrix but this may not be feasible if the number of matrix materials is too large. Such a situation leads to the use of internal standards, that is, other elements that are added to the specimen in known amounts. There are several requirements and limitations on the use of internal standards:

(*1*) Internal standards are best suited to the measurement of elements that are present as less than about 10 % composition although they may be used for higher concentrations on some occasions. The reason for the 10 % nominal limit is that the internal standard should be added in about the same amount as the element to be determined. When more than 10 % is added, it may alter the effective matrix and introduce errors in the determination.

(*2*) The internal standard element should be close to the desired element in atomic number subject to certain limitations. If Z is the atomic number of the element to be determined, elements $Z \pm 1$ will have nearly the same absorption and enhancement coefficients with respect to the matrix. Thus a given measured intensity will correspond to the same composition of the standard element and the desired element. Caution should be used in adding standards two or three atomic numbers away from the desired element because of the likelihood of selective absorption or enhancement between the standard and the desired element. For instance, rhodium is not a suitable standard for molybdenum because the $\mathrm{Rh}\,K_\alpha$ radiation excites the molybdenum strongly. Likewise, yttrium is not a suitable standard because it absorbs the $\mathrm{Mo}\,K_\alpha$ radiation strongly. Some workers have used as internal standards, elements whose L radiation is close to the K radiation of the desired element in wavelength. This is not a good choice if it can be avoided because the absorption properties of the standard will be different from those of the desired element, and also because the L line intensities do not have the same relation to composition as do the K lines (L lines are only about $\frac{1}{5}$ to $\frac{1}{8}$ as strong as K lines at the same wavelength).

(*3*) Perhaps most important, the internal standard must be made homogeneous in the specimen. This may be difficult or in some cases impossible to accomplish if particle size is important and cannot be reduced sufficiently by grinding.

5.9. *Adding Known Amounts of the Desired Element*

Sometimes it may happen that there is no suitable element available that will serve as a good internal standard. Then the best technique is to add a known amount of the same element that is to be determined to one aliquot of the unknown. If the unknown is thought to contain about 5 % niobium, one might add 1 % niobium to one aliquot of the specimen. By measuring the niobium intensity from the unknown and the unknown plus 1 % samples, Eq. 5-17 may be used to solve for the composition, C.

$$I_C/I_{C+1\%} = C/(C+1 \%) \qquad (5\text{-}17)$$

where I_C and $I_{C+1\%}$ are the measured intensities; C and $C+1 \%$ are the inknown and unknown plus 1 % compositions. This method depends again on a straight line approximation of intensity versus composition over a small concentration range and is usually justified.

One additional point should be made in regard to internal standards for limited specimens. As discussed in Sec. 5.6, for limited specimens, the intensity is proportional to the absolute amount of the element present and there is no matrix effect. Any standard element added need not approximate the unknown in absolute amount as long as the added element is also of limited quantity. The ratio of unknown and standard intensities is linear over a wide range. The same criterion holds for comparison standards as well as internal standards.

Precision in Quantitative Analysis

5.10. *Sources of Error and their Approximate Values*

In quantitative analysis, one must always realize that the answer obtained is subject to certain errors. The precision of the answer depends on all of the experimental errors that will be discussed below. The accuracy of the answer, that is, the agreement with known composition, depends on some absolute method of analysis such as wet chemistry because the x-ray method is not absolute in itself. It will be assumed that the x-ray results may be adjusted to chemical values by suitable calibration curves so that the accuracy is approximately as good as the precision.

Several factors must be considered in discussing precision: primary x-ray tube operating conditions; spectrometer adjustment; detector statistics; estimating unknown composition from calibration curves; and specimen inhomogeneities. Each of these factors may be expressed in terms of the standard deviation, σ_i, it contributes to the result. Then the overall standard deviation σ may be calculated by the usual rule for adding variance (standard deviation squared).

$$\sigma^2 = \sum \sigma_i^2 \qquad (5\text{-}18)$$

Of all the contributions to the standard deviation listed, only that from detector statistics is easily calculated; the rest must be determined experimentally. Detector statistics was discussed in Secs. 4.9 to 4.12 and the standard deviation for a measurement is just $\sqrt{N}$, where N is the total number of counts registered by the detector. That this is a legitimate expression is shown by Table 5-1 where several readings at total counts of 10^3, 10^4 and 10^5 are com-

TABLE 5-1

Standard Deviation of Repeated x-Ray Measurements at Various Total Counts

1600 counts			10200 counts			92000 counts		
Time, secs	Dev.	Dev.²	Time, secs	Dev.	Dev.²	Time, secs	Dev.	Dev.²
15.2	0.4	0.16	160	0.4	0.16	1458	2	4
14.0	0.8	0.64	159	0.6	0.36	1460	4	16
15.2	0.4	0.16	163	3.4	11.56	1460	4	16
15.0	0.2	0.04	160	0.4	0.16	1461	5	25
14.8	0.0	0.00	160	0.4	0.16	1452	4	16
15.0	0.2	0.04	157	2.6	6.76	1451	5	25
14.2	0.6	0.36	160	0.4	0.16	1453	3	9
14.8	0.0	0.00	160	0.4	0.16			
15.2	0.4	0.16	159	0.6	0.36			
15.0	0.2	0.04	158	1.6	2.56			
14.84			159.6			1455		
σ_{obs}	2.9 %		σ_{obs}	0.99 %		σ_{obs}	0.30 %	
σ_{exp}	2.5 %		σ_{exp}	1.0 %		σ_{exp}	0.33 %	

pared. The agreement is very satisfactory between the observed and expected values.

Some of the other contributions to standard deviation have been measured by various workers, and work is going on in ASTM committee E-2 to evaluate the factors as observed by a number of laboratories cooperatively. The ASTM results are not available yet but Table 5-2 shows values obtained by the author for the

TABLE 5-2

Contributions to the Deviation in x-Ray Measurements
(For Compositions Greater than 1 %)

Source of deviation	Usual range, %	Good normal value, %
Variations in x-ray power supply	0.2	0.2
Setting tube voltage and current	0.2–0.8	0.3
Positioning x-ray spectrometer at x-ray line peak	0.1–1.0	0.3
Detector statistics	0.1–3.0	0.5
Estimating composition	0.1–2.0	0.5
Inhomogeneities in specimen	0.1–10.0	0.5

several factors. By taking the values in the last column of the table and adding according to Eq. 5-18, the overall precision is seen to be about 1 % if all factors are operative. In many cases, the second and third items of Table 5-2 may not enter into the precision because it will not be necessary to adjust the operating conditions or spectrometer in comparing the unknowns with the standards. Then the precision becomes about 0.9 % which is not really much improvement.

The values above show what may be expected from the x-ray method when no special precautions are taken. Individual workers will find that on particular problems they will be able to attain 0.2 or 0.3 % of the amount present for compositions of the order of 1 % or greater. When results must be duplicated from one laboratory to another, caution should be used in stating precision to better than 0.5 % of the amount present unless the particular method of analysis has been especially well standardized.

References

1. L. von Hamos, *Arkiv f. Matematik, Astronomi, och Fysik* **31a**, article No. 25 (1945).
2. H. J. Beattie and R. M. Brissey, *Anal. Chem.* **26**, 980 (1954).
3. J. Sherman, *Spectrochim. Acta* **7**, 283 (1955).
4. J. W. Kemp and G. Andermann, Applied Research Laboratories (Glendale, Cal.) report of 1 Sept. 1955.
5. T. N. Rhodin, *Anal. Chem.* **27**, 1857 (1955).

CHAPTER 6

APPLICATIONS AND SPECIMEN TECHNIQUES

6.1. *The Twelve Types of Applications*

The foregoing chapters have attempted to help the analyst become familiar with the subject matter of fluorescent x-ray spectroscopy and with the equipment and techniques involved in its application as an analytical tool. As an analytical tool, its value depends on the practical problems for which it may be used. In order to discuss these practical applications they will be divided into groups according to the physical state of the specimen, the wavelength range of the x-rays, and the concentrations of the elements. The twelve groups to be considered here are: (*1*) alloys; (*2*) minerals and ores; (*3*) powders; (*4*) glass and ceramics; (*5*) liquids; (*6*) plating; (*7*) inhomogeneous specimens; (*8*) low concentrations; (*9*) limited total quantity; (*10*) light elements; (*11*) dynamic systems; (*12*) continuous process control. Applications of the electron probe microanalyzer are considered separately in Chapter 7 although some of them are closely related to items 7 and 9 above. Naturally there is overlapping of some of the twelve groups and some specimens will fall into several groups. It should be emphasized again that x-ray spectrochemical analysis does not depend on any of the chemical properties of the elements or on the compounds in which they are present. For this reason, *the techniques discussed are not limited to any specific elements used as examples but are equally valid for other elements that satisfy the physical requirements and have characteristic wavelengths in the proper range.*

Specimen preparation and interpretation of data are just as important as good equipment in the successful application of x-ray methods. The specimen size and shape will depend on the particular equipment used and many variations are possible. Unless the problem is specifically concerned with limited specimens, the

71

specimen should be effectively infinitely thick. That is, it should be thick enough so that any further increase in thickness will not result in any further increase in emitted x-ray intensity. Eqs. 5-5 and 5-6 of Chapter 5 indicated the mathematical considerations relating intensity to thickness. In general, if the specimen is of the order of $\frac{1}{8}$ inch thick, it may be considered infinitely thick and it is not necessary to go through the equations to evaluate the intensity. For any application it is good practice to measure both the line and background intensity, to correct for background, and if necessary to make use of the statistics discussed in Secs. 4.9 to 4.12 in order to calculate the expected precision.

Metals and Alloys

6.2.   *Alloy Steels*: *Relative Intensity of K and L Spectra*

Steels of various types are among the most common and most important alloys. High temperature alloys, although not really steels because iron may be a minor constituent, do contain many of the same elements such as nickel, chromium, manganese, cobalt, vanadium, and molybdenum, and the same techniques apply. Argon-filled Geiger or proportional counters are well suited for measuring all of the elements above except molybdenum; krypton-filled detectors are better suited for molybdenum and also for niobium if it is present. Counting rates with either flat or curved crystal x-ray optics are of the order of 1000 cps for each 1 % composition. Thus compositions in the range from 1 % to 100 % may easily be determined to about 0.5 % to 1 % of the amount present for counting intervals of one minute at the line peak and at a suitable background position. This coefficient of variation of the order of 1 % is often a practical limit for precision even though counting rates would indicate greater precision. This is because composition variation from one specimen to another, differences in surface texture, etc. come into the picture and limit the precision.

For the composition range from about 1 % down to 0.1 %, precision of about 2–3 % of the amount present is attainable with the one minute counting intervals. Determinations below the 0.1 % composition level have less precision because of the low counting

rate relative to the background. Nevertheless, the limit of detectability as discussed in Sec. 4.12 is often as low as 0.001 % depending on the particular element and the matrix effect.

Specimens are prepared by first sawing or cutting to size and
then abrading the surface down to about #00 emery paper or to
about 30–50 microinch finish. Surfaces rougher than this are sometimes satisfactory if the preparation is the same for all specimens.
Mounts for rotating the specimen during examination are available
but should be used to average out slight inhomogeneities of the
specimen and primary x-ray intensity rather than to correct for
irregular surfaces. Quantitative analysis is usually accomplished
from calibration curves prepared from known standards. Calculation of composition is also possible using the equations in Sec. 5.2.
Table 6-1 shows results obtained by Kemp and Andermann [1] using
approximations similar to Sec. 5.4.

TABLE 6-1

Stainless Steels

Element	Composition range (%)	Average difference chemical − x-ray (%)
Fe	68–98	0.3
	49–95	0.3
Cr	7–20	0.09
	7–20	0.11
Ni	2–12	0.06
	5–20	0.10
Mn	0–1.5	0.025
	0–1.7	0.02
Mo	0–3	0.02

For alloys containing high atomic number elements where the
L spectra must be used, the intensities are lower than the K series
for the same wavelengths by a factor of about 5–8. Table 6-2 shows
recent comparative measurements on the K and L spectra of
several elements. Measurements with a tungsten target primary
x-ray tube, an argon-filled Geiger counter and a LiF analyzing
crystal gave the results shown in Table 6-2.

TABLE 6-2

Comparison of K and L Series Intensities at the Same Wavelength

Wavelength	Element lines	Ratio of intensity [a]
1.3 A	Ga K/Pt L	4.7
1.5 A	Cu K/Ta L	5.8
2.1 A	Mn K/Sm L	8.7
2.8 A	Ti K/Ba L	7.6

[a] The numbers are the ratio of the K series line intensity to the L series intensity.

Minerals and Ores

6.3.   Techniques for Various Minerals

Minerals and ores may be examined either as solids or as powders. A great deal of work has been done by both the Bureau of Mines College Park Station [2] and by the U.S. Geological Survey [3] in establishing standards and evaluating x-ray spectrochemical analysis for all types of minerals and ores from the very light elements of aluminum, magnesium, and silicon to the heaviest elements thorium and uranium. Two difficulties occur in these applications: (1) the matrix in which the elements of interest must be measured varies greatly in composition and thus in its effect on the intensity versus composition relations; (2) the material is often inhomogeneous, requiring analysis of small areas or veins ranging from a few microns to a few millimeters in size. These difficulties tend to reduce the precision of the analysis unless rather careful techniques are used. One means of overcoming the matrix effect is the judicious use of internal standards as was discussed in Sec. 5.8.

Adler and Axelrod [3] found for example that the use of the thallium L_{β_1} line for the analysis of thorium allowed a precision of 1–2 % of the amount present and this may be considered typical. Mortimore, Romans and Tews [4] used hafnium and zirconium as standards for ores containing of the order of 0.05 % niobium and 0.2 % tantalum. They dissolved the ores, added the internal standards, and precipitated the metals as hydroxides. Their precision was about 5 % of the amount present at the 2 % composition level. Campbell and Carl [2] found that by first determining the equivalent uranium content of thorium-uranium ores by radioactivity measurements and then determining the U/Th ratio by fluorescent x-ray spectroscopy, they were able to eliminate matrix effects and to achieve a precision of 10 % of the amount present in the composition range about 0.5 %. Despujols,[5] in analyzing zinc and lead in ores, added known amounts of the same elements according to the technique discussed in Sec. 5.9 and achieved precision of 5–10 % of the amount present in the composition range of about 1 %. He used curved crystal optics with aluminum analyzing crystals.

Specimen preparation with minerals and ores is more varied than with alloys. For direct examination of solid specimens, grinding and abrading to produce a flat surface is the same as for alloys. When the material is to be powdered for examination, Adlter and Axelrod [3] found it was necessary to grind below −200 mesh size in order to obtain consistant and reproducable results.

6.4. *Inhomogeneous Mineral Specimens*

For direct examination of inhomogeneous mineral specimens, Adler and Axelrod [6] used curved LiF crystal optics and masked the primary beam so that an area only 0.5 mm in diameter was irradiated on the surface of a flat specimen. By translating the specimen past the primary beam, they were able to map out the concentrations of iron, cobalt and selenium in a pyrite ore as shown in Fig. 6-1. They found that selenium varied independently of the iron and that cobalt only occurred where there was selenium but not everywhere that selenium occurred. Their limiting area with fluorescent x-ray spectroscopy was about 0.5 mm but this may be further reduced to the neighborhood of a 1 micron area when direct electron excitation is used in the electron probe microanalyzer described in Chapter 7.

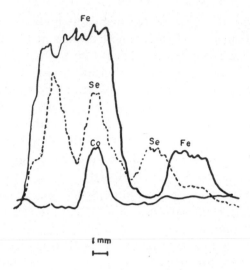

Fig. 6-1. Variation in iron, cobalt, and selenium in a pyrite ore. The specimen was translated past a masked-down x-ray beam of ½ mm diameter.

Powders

6.5.   *Direct Preparation; the Borax Bead Technique*

Powder specimens include pigments, abrasives, dusts, etc. Precision is similar to that for alloys for elements having the same wavelength range. Often the elements of interest occur as oxides, sulfides, etc., and it is necessary to calibrate intensity with internal or external standards. Grinding to reduce particle size may be necessary as with the ores discussed in Sec. 6.3. Although it is possible to examine powders in a loose condition, it is often of advantage to compact them into briquettes either with or without a binder. A small hydraulic press such as is used in preparing metallurgical specimen mounts for polishing is economical and has sufficient pressure (2000-5000) for compaction of most powders. Compaction reduces overall intensity variations from one specimen to another and also makes it easier to store the specimens for future reference. Of course, the comparison standards should be prepared in the same way as the unknowns.

Dilution of powder with inert material such as starch was found by Campbell and Carl [7] to allow wider ranges of composition to be measured conveniently. Dilution and mixing also tends to break up agglomerates in specimens if it happens that one component tends to gather in lumps. At other times, conversion to oxides makes it possible to grind and mix metal elements more homogeneously. Chemical solution and re-precipitation may be used to remove unwanted compounds and improve homogeneity. This is especially valuable for powders where heavy and light elements are not distributed uniformly within the particles or are contained in particles of different sizes. Flat platelets or long needle particles may make the addition of internal standards difficult.

Some workers favor the borax bead technique [8] for all specimens where it is feasible. In this technique, known weights of specimens are fused with borax by heating over a Meker gas burner in a platinum crucible, and flat disks of reproducible size are formed on cooling. Standards are prepared in the same way. Certainly one advantage is that the specimens are impervious to further change with time and may be stored easily for future reference. It is also possible to vary the weight of specimen added and so to control the absolute intensity measured in the case of widely varying compositions. While the borax bead technique is not advocated as a cure-all for all specimen preparation problems, the analyst should be aware of it and have it available for suitable specimens.

Glass and Ceramics

6.6. *Application to Minor Constituents and to Ancient Glass*

In glass and ceramics, there is usually not as much interest in quantitative analysis of the major constituents as there was in the previous applications discussed. Rather, the problem is one of determining impurities or low concentration components. In glass, these low concentrations are important in determining the color and transmission properties, and sometimes only semi-quantitative analysis is required. Likewise in ceramics such as porcelain enamel for coating metals, it is often the low concentration components that determine firing characteristics and the surface appearance which is so important. Fortunately, in both these materials the matrix consists primarily of low atomic number elements such as calcium, potassium, oxygen, etc., and so matrix absorption does not interfere with measurement of small percentages of the elements of interest. For instance, Bacon and Popoff [9] were able to analyze for cadmium, zinc, selenium, zirconium, silver, iron, antimony, arsenic, rhodium platinum, barium, potassium, sulfur, calcium, and titanium in glass with precision ranging from 0.8 % of the amount present for major constituents to several per cent for minor constituents. Similarly, Patrick [10] analyzed for the order of 0.1 % iron (as Fe_2O_3) in glaze frits with a precision of about 5 % of the amount present. He also analyzed for the order of 0.2 % niobium in titanium base enamel with a precision of 7 % of the amount present. Other application in ceramics include lead in glaze frits and the nickel-cobalt-rich layer deposited on the steel surface during the firing of the ground coat for enameling. Under the ground coat, quantities of nickel and cobalt of the order of 0.01 to 0.05 grams per square foot were observed with a precision of 5 % of the amount present.

Another interesting application of x-ray spectrochemical analysis is its use for analyzing ancient glass. The archeologists would like to know the source of raw material that went into the making of ancient glass so that they may postulate on trade conditions that existed among ancient civilizations and thus establish links between different peoples. The materials used often contained small quantities of elements that were indigenous to certain regions or countries. The presence of these elements in the glass or ceramic art objects therefore points definitely to the source of the material. The nondestructive nature of x-ray spectroscopy makes it valuable because the priceless relics cannot be destroyed for wet chemical or emission spectroscopy analysis. R. W. Smith,[11] the head of the Ancient Glass group of the International Society of Archeology has been most interested in establishing the possibilities of x-ray spectroscopy for this purpose and has achieved some promising results to be published soon in the journal *Archeology*.

Liquids

6.7. *Types of Cells and Limitations*

One of the first applications for x-ray analysis of liquids was the determination of lead and bromine in aviation gasoline.[12] The problem is of primary concern to the military because they must often store gasoline for indefinite periods of time. On standing, there is precipitation of the lead with consequent reduction of the octane rating of the gasoline. By containing the gasoline in Mylar covered plastic cells, the lead and bromine were easily determined in concentrations from .02 to 0.5 % with precision of about 1 % of the amount present. Calibration curves prepared from known standards were used for the quantitative analysis. Refinements of the technique for various base fuel composition and the extension to the measurement of chlorine as well as bromine were soon developed.[13]

In any liquid analysis, it is important that bubbles do not form next to the Mylar and thus change the effective surface of the liquid. It is often desirable to use the inverted spectrograph described by Tomaino and De Pietro[14] in which the specimen is mounted above the x-ray tube and irradiated through a thin Mylar window on the bottom of the cell. This precludes gas bubbles from forming at the interface. Of course for many liquids there is little or no problem with evaporation, and then windowless cells may be used with the liquid level maintained at a fixed position. For some specimens it is possible to change the liquid to a solid with resulting convenience in specimen handling. Lithium stearate, for instance, may be used to change oils to grease without increasing the matrix absorption noticeably. Freezing may also be of advantage especially if a helium or vacuum spectrometer is being used for measuring light elements. For instance, with water solutions at room temperature (20°C) the vapor pressure of water is about 17.5 mm of mercury and this much water vapor absorbs about 58 % of, say, $Mg K_\alpha$ radiation in a 20 cm path length of helium. The vapor pressure of ice (−20°C) on the other hand, is only 0.75 mm of mercury resulting in only 4 % absorption. Thus the usable intensity is increased from 42 % to 96 %, or by a factor of about 2, by freezing the water.

One of the problems with liquid specimens is the high background intensity caused by the more intense scattering from the light elements of which most liquids consist. Pulse height discrimination results in a reduction of the background by factors of 2 to 50, depending on the wavelength range and the type of detector. However it does not eliminate the problem. Another problem is the precipitation of certain components from the liquid either by the action of the x-ray beam or because the specimen is really an emulsion or suspension instead of a true solution. On the advantage side for liquid specimens is the ease of adding internal standards and the control of concentration by dilution or partial distillation. Liquids also make an ideal starting point for ion exchange and chemical enrichment techniques as will be discussed in Sec. 6.10.

Plating

6.8. *Range of Thickness*

Measurement of tin plating on steel was the application that really led to the rejuvenation of interest in x-ray spectroscopy in the 1940's, and it is still one of the most important applications in commerce, where it is used for continuous process control. The thickness range of interest is from 0.1 to 2.5 pounds per base box (0.18 to 4.5×10^{-4} cm).[15] The system of tin and steel is a particularly simple one because iron and tin are separated so far in atomic number and thus in x-ray wavelength. The exciting voltage on the primary x-ray tube may be set at 25 kev to excite iron efficiently without exciting the tin spectrum at all. The tin has a high absorption coefficient for iron radiation and thus the measured iron intensity is very sensitive to tin thickness. Beeghly[16] showed that even without collimation of the emitted radiation, satisfactory measurements in a practical sense were feasible. Of course, proportional counters with pulse amplitude discrimination and nondispersive optics are ideal for this application.

Zemany and Liebhafsky[17] have discussed three methods of measuring plating thickness including the nondispersive optics used by Beeghly. The other two methods use dispersive optics and measure the characteristic x-rays either from the base layer or from the plating material itself.[18] Birks, Brooks, and Friedman [19] showed that multiple plating layers could be determined non-destructively by first measuring the characteristic x-rays from the outermost layer and determining its absolute thickness from calibration plating standards. Next the characteristic x-rays from the second layer down are measured and corrected for absorption by the outer layer. A family of calibration curves is necessary as shown in Fig. 6-2 to account for variations in the outer layer thick-

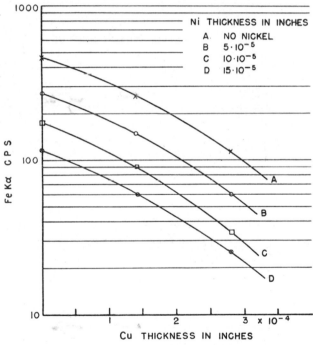

Fig. 6-2. Family of calibration curves for a double plating of copper and nickel on iron. The iron x-ray intensity is plotted against the thickness of copper which is the first layer plated on the iron. The nickel thickness is first determined from a calibration curve of nickel intensity vs. nickel thickness so that the proper curve of the family may be chosen.

ness. If the specimen contains only two plating layers on the base
layer, the characteristic lines of the base layer may also be used
along with those of the outermost layer to determine the intermediate layer thickness. About three plating layers is the limit of
the method because complications arise due to interelement effects
such as mutual excitation from one layer to another.

Considering the various methods and combinations of methods,
plating layers from about 1 micron to perhaps 0.5 mm may be
determined with precision ranging from about 50 % for the thin-
nest layers to 1 % for intermediate thickness around 0.002 inches
and back to 50 % for the thickest layers around 0.5 mm. The
plating material and the base material will cause variation in both
the thickness measurable and the possible precision.

Inhomogeneous Specimens

6.9.   *Large and Small Scale Inhomogeneities*

Two inhomogeneous types of specimens should be considered.
Either the average overall composition is desired or the variations
in composition are important and must be considered. Brief mention of the second type was made in Sec. 6.4 where it was not the
average composition of the mineral that was desired but the par-
tition of elements within the specimen. A similar situation existed
in the examination of weld beads at NRL wherein the variation of
manganese, chromium and nickel across the boundary gave information about the quality of the weld. Again a masked-down
x-ray beam and curved crystal optics were used with the specimen
translated past the primary beam. The irradiated area was limited
to a circle either 0.15 mm or 0.5 mm diameter, usually the latter.
Fig. 6-3 shows the variation in chromium and nickel across a weld
bead in 18 % Cr–8 % Ni stainless steel. The weld rod contained
25 % Cr and 20 % Ni; thus both chromium and nickel increase in
intensity in the weld zone. Subtraction of the background intensity
would make the change in chromium more apparent. In another
low alloy steel weld, the intensities listed in Table 6-3 were obtained and compared with the composition in the parent metal and the
weld zone. The correspondence between composition and x-ray

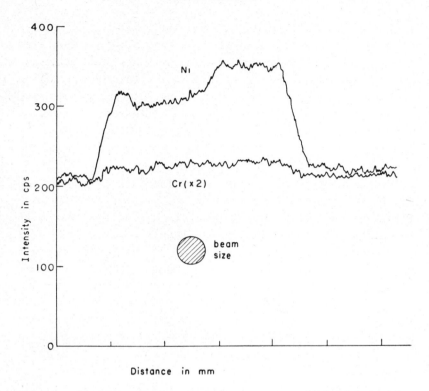

Fig. 6-3. x-Ray intensity from scanning across a weld bead in stainless steel. The nickel content was about 8 % in the parent metal and about 20 % in the weld. The chromium content went from 18 % in the parent metal to about 25 % in the weld. An x-ray beam of ½ mm diameter was used for the scanning.

TABLE 6-3

Composition and x-Ray Intensity for Low-Alloy Steel Weld

Element	% composition		x-Ray intensity	
	Parent metal	Weld bead	Parent metal	Weld bead
Cr	1.24	0.7	13	6
Mn	0.22	0.6	16	43
Ni	2.8	2.2	293	193

intensity is nearly linear for each element.

Going back to the problem where an average composition must be measured for inhomogeneous specimens, several techniques may be used to determine whether or not the specimen is inhomogeneous and what the average composition is. If a material such as an ingot or a powder mixture is suspected of being inhomogeneous, it is necessary to make a sufficient number of measurements so that statistical fluctuations may be separated from composition differences. Two cases arise:

(*1*) Inhomogeneities over distances of several centimeters will require that eight to ten specimens be selected judiciously from different parts of the total material; for ingots, they should be taken from the top, the bottom, the edges, and several positions in between. First, a single one of the specimens should be chosen and the instrumental statistical variations determined. These include not only the detector fluctuations but also variations arising from removing and replacing the specimen in the holder and variations due to setting the spectrometer at the x-ray line peak for each element. Therefore, the single specimen should be removed and replaced between measurements. Ten repeated measurements of this specimen will allow the overall standard deviation, σ_{obs}, for each element to be calculated using Eq. 6-1 which merely repeats Eq. 4-1 of Chapter 4.

$$\sigma_{obs} = [\sum(x_i - \mu)^2/(n-1)]^{\frac{1}{2}} \tag{6-1}$$

where $n = 10$ is the number of measurements, x_i is an individual measurement on a particular element, and μ is the average of the n measurements on that element. The reader is referred back to Sec. 4.9 for a more complete discussion of the statistics. Next, all of the rest of the specimens chosen are measured in the usual manner and the standard deviation of the values found for each chemical element using Eq. 6-1 where now n different specimens are substituted for the n measurements on the same specimen. For a given element, if the standard deviation among the eight to ten specimens exceeds the instrumental standard deviation for that element by a factor of 2 or more, then it may be assumed that the material is inhomogeneous in that element. An average over the eight to ten specimens will, however, give a reasonably good estimate of the average composition.

(2) Inhomogeneities may exist over a few millimeters of material but average out over large distances. This is often true for banded alloys that have been improperly rolled or forged. Now it is well known that the intensity of the primary beam is not constant over the type of specimen used with flat crystal optics, and repositioning an inhomogeneous specimen in the primary beam will cause variation in the fluorescent intensity. For most specimens, it will be sufficient to reposition the specimen four times, turning it 90° each time, to average out the small scale inhomogeneities and the varying intensity of the primary beam. Of course the specimen should be square or round rather than rectangular in order to do this conveniently. Curved crystal optics and a masked down beam (Sec. 6.4) allow easier determination of these small scale inhomogeneities if the equipment is available.

Low Concentrations

6.10. *Minimum Detectable Limit for Direct Measurements*

When interest in fluorescent x-ray spectroscopy was first revived in the 1940's, it was considered to be primarily suited for measuring compositions from say 1 % to 100 %. However, the nondestructive nature of the technique and the simplicity of interpretation of the x-ray spectra made it only natural to push the method to its limit in the low concentration range and minimum detectable limit. Measurement of low concentrations depends on both the absolute intensity available and the line-to-background ratio. Improvements in x-ray tube power, analyzing crystals and detectors have greatly increased the absolute intensity available, but have done far less to improve the line-to-background ratio. For most of the low concentration measurements, it will be the detector statistics that determine the precision and the detectability rather than the other instrumental statistics discussed in Sec. 5.10 of Chapter 5.

The coefficient of variation, σ %, for a determination was given by Eq. 4-2 of Chapter 4 which is repeated below.

$$\sigma \% = (N_l + N_b)^{\frac{1}{2}}/(N_l - N_b) \tag{6-2}$$

where N_l and N_b are the total number of counts at the peak and background positions respectively. The minimum detectable limit was defined in Sec. 4.12 of Chapter 4. The definition says that to be detectable, the line must be above background by at least three standard deviations of the background. Using this criterion, we may give typical order of magnitude values for the minimum detectable limit in parts per million as shown in Table 6-4 and taken from results in the literature. The values given in Table 6-4

TABLE 6-4

Minimum Detectable Limit

Not concentrated	Concentrated
10 ppm [a]	0.01 ppm [b]
100 ppm for light element in heavy matrix	
1 ppm for medium element in light matrix	

[a] ppm = parts per million.

[b] There is of course no absolute lower limit if large enough starting quantities are used. There are however practical limitations on both quantity and preparation time; the value listed represents a limit actually achieved in what is considered a practical analytical procedure.

are, of course, only representative and are affected by a number of factors. For instance, the L spectral lines are only about $\frac{1}{5}$ to $\frac{1}{8}$ as intense as the K spectral lines in the same wavelength range as was shown in Table 6-2 above. Also, some elements are excited strongly by the matrix, such as titanium by iron in steel. This may raise the intensity of an element by a factor of 5. The column marked "not concentrated" represents measurements of an element *in situ*, and the column marked "concentrated" refers to separation of the element from the matrix by some extraction procedure such as ion exchange [20] or chemical precipitation.[21] The details of these procedures vary greatly with the particular specimens and cannot be discussed here.

One of the practical applications involving low concentrations was the determination of nickel, iron, and vanadium on alumina-silica gasoline cracking catalysts by Dyroff and Skiba.[22] They measured iron in the range from 0.1 % to 1.0 % and nickel and vanadium from 0.002 to 0.1 %. Another application was the measurement of arsenic in steel in the range down to 0.001 % by Cavanagh[23] who dissolved five grams of specimen in acid and precipitated an internal standard, germanium, along with the arsenic. He collected the precipitate on glass filter paper which he then used as the specimen support directly and so eliminated having to handle the precipitate and the possibility of losing some of it. Ion exchange has many possibilities for low concentration measurements but requires careful calibration and often long specimen preparation times as Grubb and Zemany [20] showed in collecting one microgram or less of iron, zinc, manganese, and cobalt on cation membranes. Two to three hours were necessary to attain equilibrium, and even then they were not sure that all of the desired element had been collected without further tests. They found that the capacity of the ion exchange membranes must be several times greater than the amount of the ions to be collected in order to reach equilibrium in reasonable lengths of time.

Limited Total Quantity

6.11. *Limit with Crystal Optics and with the Electron Probe*

The minimum detectable limit for concentrated specimens leads directly to the problem of limited total quantity although limited specimens may arise from many other causes such as airborne dusts, evidence in criminal cases, corrosion products on surfaces, and even plating layers. Whenever the specimen is less than effectively infinitely thick, (see Sec. 5.2) it may be considered of limited total quantity. Calibration standards require care in preparation because they should approximate the quantity of the unknown specimen. Often internal standards of known quantity are the most suitable for quantitative analysis. Several situations arise depending on the form and amount of the specimen. If the specimen can be evaporated or precipitated from solution or is already present as a thin film, it should be mounted on a thin backing layer such as Mylar. The primary beam should be allowed to pass on through the specimen mount and be trapped by baffles to reduce background scattering to a minimum. Using thin oxide layers stripped from stainless steel, Rhodin [24] was able to measure microgram quantities of iron, nickel, and chromium by this technique; his results are given in Table 6-5. Background values are

TABLE 6-5

x-Ray Intensities from Microgram Quantities

Element	Intensity [a]
Cr	8.5
Fe	16.5
Ni	26.8

[a] Numbers are in counts per second/micrograms per square centimeter.

very dependent on specific experimental conditions and the analyst must remember to take account of background intensity in evaluating actual data. His measurements also showed that for these very limited specimens, there is practically no matrix effect and the intensity of each element is directly related to the absolute quantity present. Thus the problem of standards for such specimens is simplified. Once the intensity versus quantity relationship is established for an element, quantitative analysis may be performed on any composition as long as the experimental conditions are not changed.

If the specimen is naturally in a form suitable for use as a point or line source, curved-crystal x-ray optics will usually yield appreciably greater intensity than flat-crystal optics. In the *limiting* case when the specimen is of the minimum detectable quantity and of minute physical dimensions, curved-crystal optics will be expected to yield almost 100 times the intensity of flat-crystal optics. This is because the solid angle utilized from a point source with curved-crystal optics is about 100 times larger than the solid angle allowed by the collimator required for flat-crystal optics. For this limiting circumstance, Table 6-6 shows the order of

magnitude of the minimum detectable limit in grams. As shown
in the table, the electron probe extends the limit far beyond any-
thing remotely possible by fluorescent x-ray excitation. The
electron probe is discussed in detail in Chapter 7.

TABLE 6-6

Usual Minimum Detectable Quantities

Flat crystal	Curved crystal	Electron probe
10^{-6} g	10^{-8} g	10^{-14} g

When the specimen is as large as 10^{-3} grams, curved-crystal
optics yield intensities comparable to the intensities from full
sized specimens with flat-crystal optics as shown in Table 6-7.[25]

TABLE 6-7

x-Ray Intensity from an Aluminum Specimen Containing 0.52 % Iron
and 0.81 % Manganese

Element	Flat crystal optics extended specimen	Curved crystal optics 1 mg specimen
Fe	280 cps	360 cps
Mn	190	160

Thus a 1 mg specimen may be considered as a full-sized specimen
when it is mounted on a capillary and used as a line source on a
focusing spectrometer.

6.12. Preparation of Limited Specimens

In preparing limited specimens for curved crystal optics, capillary mounting is often the simplest technique. The capillary acts
as a line source on the focusing circle; it may be positioned very
close to the primary x-ray tube and so receives a high flux of
exciting radiation. The choice of capillary material for mounting
the specimen may be varied with the problem at hand. If fine wire
is used and if it is of uniform diameter, the x-ray line from the
wire may be used as an internal standard. Besides wire for mount-

ing the specimens, glass or plastic fibers are also simple and sometimes satisfactory, but the background scattering may be too high
for some plastic fibers. The size of the capillary should be well
under 0.5 mm and the specimen should be powdered in a micro-
mortar and stuck to the capillary with grease or glue or rubber
cement diluted in benzene. In any case, no more adhesive than
necessary should be used because it increases the background
scattering. The x-ray beam must be masked down so that only the
specimen is irradiated to prevent air scattering, and a beam trap
should be used behind the specimen.

Light Elements

6.13. *Excitation of Light Elements: Fluorescent Yield*

In x-ray spectrochemical analysis, the term "light elements"
usually refers to the elements from sodium (11) to titanium (22).
For these elements, the characteristic x-rays fall in the wavelength
range 11.9 to 2.7 A and are so strongly attenuated even by air
that most of the radiation is lost before reaching the detector unless helium or hydrogen gas or a vacuum path is used. A second
problem with the light elements is the choice of a suitable analyzing crystal because the interplanar spacing, d, of LiF, for instance
is too small. That is, the Bragg equation,

$$n\lambda = 2d \sin \theta$$

requires that the spacing, $2d$, be at least λ for diffraction to occur
even at the maximum θ angle of 90°. Potassium chloride crystals
have a (200) spacing of $2d = 6.28$ A and may be used down to
phosphorus (15). Sodium iodide with a spacing of 6.46 A may be
used for the same range, but it is hygroscopic and must be kept dry
at all times. For the elements sodium, magnesium, aluminum, and
silicon none of the alkali halides have long enough spacings and
other materials are required. Some possible choices for suitable
crystals are sugar ($d = 10.6$ A), silver acetate ($d = 10$ A) mica
($d = 9$ A), but in general the diffracting power of all these crystals
is far lower than with the alkali halides resulting in loss of measured
intensity. The problem is not insurmountable because it may be

possible for organic chemists to "design" crystals of high diffracting power and suitable spacing. As yet, no attempts have been made along these lines.

The problem of exciting the light elements outside the primary x-ray tube is very important because of the absorption of exciting radiation by the beryllium windows. As was discussed in Sec. 2.6 of Chapter 2, 99.9 % of the most effective wavelength for exciting phosphorus is absorbed. Considering excitation by the whole primary x-ray spectrum, factors of ~ 6.20 times would be gained by eliminating the Be window. It will be of advantage to go to demountable x-ray tubes with the specimen located inside on the cathode shield and excited by fluorescence after the method of Coster and Druyvestyn discussed in Sec. 2.6 of Chapter 2. Then a Mylar window may be used between the x-ray tube and the vacuum spectrometer to reduce attenuation. The thin-window flow Geiger or proportional counters discussed in Sec. 4.7 of Chapter 4 offer the best possibilities for detecting the long wavelengths from the light elements. Flow rates with the commonly used 90 % argon–10 % methane proportional counter gas should be rapid at first to flush out the counter; after flushing, the rate may be reduced to the order of 0.5 to 1 cubic feet per hour [26, 27] and the pulse amplitude will remain stable. It might be thought that scintillation counters would be even better than flow counters but the best scintillation crystal at present is NaI which is very hygroscopic and must be protected by a coating that will offer at least as much attenuation as the thin windows of the flow counters.

In the excitation of light elements, there is a phenomenon which limits the intensity obtained in the characteristic spectrum. It is called the fluorescent yield. As was stated in Chapter 1, when a K electron is knocked out of an atom, another electron will replace it giving rise to one of the K series emission lines. However, in some instances, the K emission radiation may never leave the atom. It may instead knock out an L electron and thus generate the L series. This effect is also known as the Auger effect and the probability of its occurrence increases as we go to lower atomic

numbers.* It was shown by A. H. Compton [28] that 70 % of the
K radiation escapes from the atom for Z 55, but only 10 %
escapes for Z less than 20. Fig. 6-4 shows the fluorescent yield as a

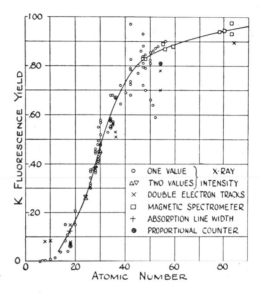

Fig. 6-4. Fluorescent yield as a function of atomic number.

function of atomic number.[29] Although recent calculations indicate that the yield may be slightly higher than Fig. 6-4 indicates
for the low atomic number end, there is no question that the intensity is far less for the light elements than for the heavy elements.
This decrease in fluorescent yield is just one more difficulty encountered in the analysis of light elements.

6.14.   *Effect of Particle Size*

Specimen preparation with the light elements requires a smoother
surface than for the heavier elements. In the case of powders, the
usual grinding to about −300 mesh size to overcome variable
absorption was found to be insufficient by Campbell and Thatcher.[27] They calculated that for calcium in tungsten ores, the particle

* The effect occurs in the target of an x-ray tube also and is one of the
reasons for lower intensity K series lines as we go to lighter element targets.

size must be of the order of 0.05 microns for 99 % of the calcium radiation to get out of the particle. Even if one were content to get only 10 % of the calcium radiation out of the particle, the particles could not be larger than 5–10 microns. If the specimen is homogeneous as in the case of alloys, there is no particle size effect, but a rough surface will cause partial shielding of some of the material with resulting variations in intensity from specimen to specimen.

Analysis of Dynamic Systems

6.15.   *Solution of Precipitation; Diffusion; Corrosion*

One of the least investigated applications of x-ray spectroscopy in the past is the variation in composition in dynamic systems. A number of such systems may be enumerated: (*1*) rate of solution of solids in solids or solids in liquids; (*2*) rate of mixing of liquids; (*3*) rate of precipitation from solution; (*4*) diffusion of metals during phase transformations; (*5*) rate of corrosion at surfaces; (*6*) rate of sublimation. The common factor in all of these problems is the measure of the rate at which some kind of reaction takes place. Wet chemical analysis or emission spectroscopy are not amenable to such processes and other methods of following changing conditions such as electrical resistivity are very limited in their scope. But with x-ray spectroscopy, it is just as easy to analyze dynamic systems as static systems. In other words, *a new dimension has been added to analytical techniques.* Not many examples are available for discussion but several specific problems may be used for illustration.

A test of the concepts was made at NRL in 1955.[30] Using a liquid cell with a Mylar window and a mask in front of the primary x-ray tube, the rate of solution of $CuSO_4$ in water was followed. Several small crystals of the salt were placed in the bottom of the cell and water was added to fill the cell. The arrangement is shown in Fig. 6-5a. The irradiated area from which fluorescent x-rays were emitted was about 0.5 mm on a side and located about 4 mm above the bottom of the cell. With the spectrometer set for Cu K_α a continuous plot of the intensity versus time was obtained as shown in Fig. 6-6. Before any coloration of the solution was

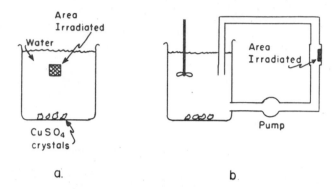

Fig. 6-5. Two arrangements for using fluorescent x-ray analysis to measure the rate of solution of a salt in a liquid. In diagram a, there is no stirring of the solution, but in diagram b, the liquid is stirred and pumped past the x-ray cell.

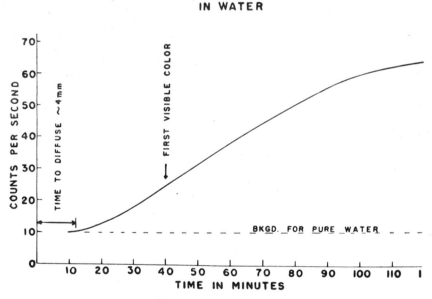

Fig. 6-6. x-Ray measurement of solution of $CuSO_4$ in water using the arrangement of Fig. 6-5a. The presence of copper is detectable by x-rays long before the first visible color can be seen.

visible, the Cu K_α x-radiation level rose to about 15 cps above background. The shape of the curve is approximately a cumulative Gaussian distribution as would be expected in a diffusion process. Obviously, many variations may be used such as in Fig. 6-5b where the liquid is stirred and pumped continuously through the x-ray cell. For quantitative analysis, calibration standards may be prepared statically and an intensity versus composition curve plotted. The x-ray data may then be converted easily to a plot of intensity versus time in the dynamic system.

Another example is the measurement of arsenic and antimony in lead by Leon and Campbell.[31] They heated the alloy in an open x-ray cell and followed the formation of the oxides on the surface of the lead. This information gives the rate of diffusion of the arsenic and antimony to the surface since the oxide is not soluble and the process is irreversible. This procedure also allowed them to determine parts per million of those two elements directly whereas they were limited to parts per thousand when the elements were distributed throughout the lead matrix.

With the 1 micron resolution of the electron probe, intermetallic diffusion may be followed using a heated specimen stage. Rates of precipitation from liquids may be studied most easily using the inverted specimen holder described by Tomaino and De Pietro.[14] Here the specimen cell is mounted above the primary x-ray tube and the thin cell window is on the bottom. Thus, precipitates will settle out of the liquid onto the cell window and give increasing intensity.

Of course there are both short and long time limitations: for processes that occur in a matter of a few seconds, the x-ray response will show statistical errors that must be accounted for in a quantitative determination; for processes requiring several hours it is more feasible to make static measurements at several points along the way.

Continuous Process Control

6.16. *Use in Feed-Back Control Systems*

Control of continuous manufacturing processes is really an application of the discussion of the previous section. However, the x-ray results are used in feed-back control systems in order to maintain a constant level rather than to measure the rates of change. The first process control was used in the tin plate industry where the x-ray spectrometer or nondispersive optics was set up on the output of the plating bath. Changes in the tin thickness are not rapid, and it is easy to vary the conditions to keep them optimum based on a continuous x-ray reading. The addition of tetraethyl lead to gasoline may also be controlled continuously by passing part of the liquid through the x-ray device and using the x-ray intensity to control the addition of the tetraethyl lead. In wire drawing, the wire coming out of the die is an ideal line source for curved crystal optics, and any variation in diameter is immediately reflected in the x-ray intensity.

6.17. *Conclusion*

The twelve groups of applications discussed in this chapter represent a wide coverage of the uses of fluorescent x-ray spectroscopy at the present time. As with any method of analysis, new equipment and techniques are being developed continuously and the old techniques are being refined and improved to give better results. Therefore, the present limits on detection and accuracy given in the various applications should not be regarded as absolute but rather as average values. If each particular problem is considered in the light of its own possibilities, the experienced analyst will be able to achieve optimum results.

References

1. J. W. Kemp and G. Andermann, *Applied Research Lab.* (*Glendale, Cal.*) *Report*, Sept. 1955.
2. H. F. Carl and W. J. Campbell, *Anal. Chem.* **27**, 1884 (1955).
3. I. Adler and J. M. Axelrod, *Spectrochim. Acta* **7**, 91 (1955).
4. D. M. Mortimore, P. A. Romans, and J. L. Tews, *Appl. Spectroscopy*, **8**, 24 (1954).
5. J. Despujols, *J. Phys. radium.* **13**, 31a (1952).
6. I. Adler and J. M. Axelrod, *Econ. Geol.* **52**, 694 (1957).
7. W. J. Campbell and H. F. Carl, *Anal. Chem.* **26**, 800 (1954).
8. F. Claisse, *Can. Dep. Mines and Tech. Surveys Report* PR No. 327 (1956).

9. J. F. Bacon and V. Popoff, *Pittsburgh Conf. on Analytical Chemistry and Applied Spectroscopy*, Paper No. 86, (1955).

10. R. F. Patrick, *J. Am. Ceram. Soc.* **35**, 189 (1952).

11. R. W. Smith, private communication.

12. L. S. Birks, E. J. Brooks, H. Friedman, and R. M. Roe, *Anal. Chem.* **22**, 1258 (1950).

13. G. T. Kokotailo and G. F. Damon, *Anal. Chem.* **25**, 1185 (1953).

14. M. Tomaino and A. De Pietro, *Norelco Reporter* **3**, 57 (1956).

15. G. E. Pellisier and E. E. Wicker, *Elec. Mfg.* **49**. 124 (1952).

16. H. F. Beeghly, *J. Electrochem. Soc.* **97**, 152 (1950).

17. P. D. Zemany and H. A. Liebhafsky, *J. Electrochem. Soc.* **103**, 157 (1956).

18. P. K. Koh and B. Caugherty, *J. Appl. Phys.* **23**, 427 (1952).

19. L. S. Birks, E. J. Brooks, and H. Friedman, *Anal. Chem.* **25**, 692 (1953).

20. W. T. Grube and P. D. Zemany, *Nature* **176**, 221 (1955).

21. A. P. Smith and F. S. Grimaldi, *Geol. Survey Bull.* **1006**, 125 (1954).

22. G. V. Dryoff and P. Skiba, *Anal. Chem.* **26**, 1774 (1954).

23. M. B. Cavanagh, *Naval Research Lab. Report* 4679 (1955).

24. T. N. Rhodin, *Anal. Chem.* **27**, 1857 (1955).

25. L. S. Birks and E. J. Brooks, *Anal. Chem.* **27**, 437 (1955).

26. C. F. Hendee, S. Fine, and W. B. Brown, *Rev. Sci. Instr.* **27**, 531 (1956).

27. W. J. Campbell and J. W. Thatcher, *U. S. Bur. Mines Report of Investigations* College Park, Md. (1958); also *Denver Research Conf.*, Denver. Colo. (Aug. 1958).

28. A. H. Compton and S. K. Allison, *X-rays in Theory and Experiment*, Van Nostrand, New York, 1935, p. 477.

29. C. E. Roos, *Phys. Rev.* **105**, 931 (1957).

30. L. S. Birks and E. J. Brooks, *Pittsburgh Conf. on Analytical Chemistry and Applied Spectroscopy*, Paper No. 75 (1956).

31. M. Leon and W. J. Campbell, *Pittsburgh Conference on Analytical Chemistry and Applied Spectroscopy*, Paper No. 70 (1958).

CHAPTER 7

THE ELECTRON PROBE MICROANALYZER

7.1. *Introduction*

By far the most important recent advance in x-ray spectrochemical analysis was the development of the electron probe
microanalyzer. The first of these instruments was built by R.
Castaing [1] about 1950. At the present time of writing, there are
perhaps a dozen instruments in the world. Each one differs slightly
from the others in design and operating characteristics, but all
of them contain the same essential features. In a sense, the
instrument is a very-fine-focus x-ray tube in which the specimen
to be analyzed is the target. However, it differs from conventional
fine-focus tubes in several important respects. First, the focal spot
may be made as small as one micron in diameter. Second, the
specimen may be moved about to bring any desired area into
position for analysis. Third, an optical microscope system is built
into the instrument for direct observation of the exact area being
analyzed. With the electron probe, it is possible to analyze individual precipitates or inclusions in metals, minerals, or other solids.
It is also possible to measure composition gradients such as occur
in alloy phases, biological tissue, or corrosion layers. Finally, it is
possible to analyze individual airborne dust particles or any other
particulate matter.

There are two reasons why the above applications could not be
accomplished by fluorescent x-ray spectroscopy. In the first place,
it would be almost impossible physically to mask down a beam of
primary x-rays so that only a one micron area on the specimen was
excited by fluorescence. In the second place, the total intensity
excited by fluorescence would be so low that reasonable counting
rates could not be obtained. With an electron beam however, it is
not difficult to focus the beam to a one micron crossover at the
specimen and the intensity excited is between 200–1000 times

greater than by fluorescence. Resulting intensities are greater than 10,000 cps from 100 % samples such as copper or iron, and in general the limit of detectability is about 0.1 % composition or less.

Because the type of instrumentation involved is not familiar to spectroscopists, a detailed treatment will be given.

Electron Optics Column

7.2. *Electron Gun Types*

Fig. 7-1 is a schematic drawing of the electron optics system necessary for forming the one micron beam of electrons.[2] The important features are the electron gun, the electromagnetic lenses, the limiting apertures, and the specimen chamber. Each of these features will be discussed in detail.

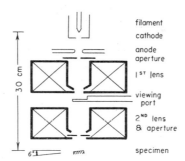

Fig. 7-1. Schematic of electron optics system for the electron probe. Electrons from the hot filament pass through two electromagnetic lens coils which act to focus a one micron beam of electrons on the specimen. Characteristic x-rays generated in the specimen emerge from the electron optics system through a beryllium window.

Fig. 7-2 shows three types of gun design. Type *a* is known as the Bricka and Bruck [3] gun. The cathode shield is very reentrant and a crossover of the electron beam occurs just below the anode. The intensity distribution of the electron beam is a three-dimensional Gaussian, and by placing an aperture of about 0.1 mm immediately below the hole in the anode, only the intense central portion of the beam is allowed to pass. The type *b* gun cathode is only slightly reentrant and the position of the crossover is less accurately known. The type c gun cathode is not reentrant. The hole in the cathode is quite large (4 mm) and the filament is back 4 or 5 mm. Again

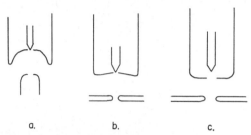

a.   b.   c.

Fig. 7-2. Three types of electron gun design. Type a has a very reentrant cathode and a crossover of the electron beam occurs just below the anode opening. Type b has a slightly reentrant cathode, while the cathode in the type c gun is not reentrant at all. The type c gun is perhaps the least efficient of the three but will operate in a stable condition with a very simple power supply.

the crossover point is not accurately known. The type c gun is less efficient than the other types, but the operating conditions are less critical. For instance, the filament need not remain accurately centered in the cathode, and slight variations in bias potential do not change the beam intensity. All of the guns operate in the saturated current condition.

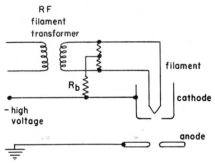

Fig. 7-3. Electronic circuit design for operating an electron gun. Stabilized negative high voltage is supplied directly to the cathode and through a bias resistor, R_B to the filament. The filament is heated by a radio frequency filament transformer, or may be heated by a 60 cycle transformer if the secondary voltage is rectified. The anode is grounded as is the body of the instrument.

Fig. 7-3 shows a typical gun circuit. Radio frequency heating is desirable for the filament. The high voltage supply is constant potential and must be stabilized to about 0.01 % or it will not be possible to maintain a 1 micron beam diameter at the specimen. Usually the voltage is variable from 10 to 50 Kev.

7.3. *Electromagnetic Lenses*

The image of the hot filament is demagnified in two stages by the two electromagnetic lenses. The first lens also controls the beam intensity reaching the specimen as shown in Fig. 7-4. If it is

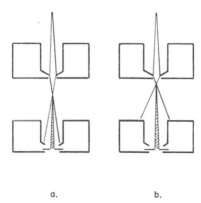

a.   b.

Fig. 7-4. Control of the beam intensity at the specimen is accomplished with the first electromagnetic lens. In the condition at the left, the first (top) lens is used as a weak lens and most of the electron beam passes through the aperture in the second (bottom) lens. In the condition at the right, the first lens is used as a strong lens and only a small portion of the electron beam passes through the second lens aperture.

operated as a weak lens, (as in Fig. 7-4a) by reducing the current in the coil, the crossover is closer to the second lens aperture and more of the beam passes through the second lens aperture. When it is operated as a strong lens as in Fig. 7-4b, only a small portion passes through the second lens aperture. The focal length of the first lens may be varied from 3 to 50 mm conveniently. The soft iron pole piece in the first lens may have a bore of about 4 mm and a gap of about 3 mm and is an end-gap type of pole piece to make the object distance large as compared to the image distance.

The second lens is much more critical in design because it limits the minimum beam size that may be achieved. Fig. 7-5 shows two

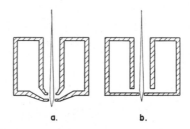

a.   b.

Fig. 7-5. Two types of pole piece design. On the left, the bore in both parts of the pole piece is the same, and the lens is symmetric. On the right, the bore in the top part of the pole piece is 5 to 10 times as large as the bore in the bottom part and the lens is asymmetric. With an asymmetric lens, the magnetic field at the specimen may be kept at a low value.

designs for the second lens pole piece. Type *a* is a symmetric pole piece with a bore of about 10 mm and a gap of about 8 mm. Type *b* is an asymmetric pole piece with the bore of the top part about 30–60 mm and of the bottom part about 6 mm; the gap is about 6 mm. Each type of pole piece has certain advantages. The type *a* pole piece has a large enough bore to permit a reflecting objective for the viewing microscope to be positioned in the pole piece itself. The type *b* pole piece shields the specimen better from the magnetic field of the magnetic lens so that there is less interaction with ferro-magnetic specimens, but it does not allow for a reflecting objective because of the small bore in the bottom part. Both types of pole piece are suitable for a working distance from the lens to specimen of the order of 1 to 1.5 cm.

7.4.   *Limiting Factors in Forming a 1 micron Beam*

There are two limiting factors in formation of a 1 micron beam and both of them are controlled by the second lens pole piece. The first is astigmatism. If the bore of the pole piece is slightly elliptical or if there are pores or inclusions in the iron near the surface, the magnetic field will not be symmetric and the image will be eliptical. It is necessary to reduce the astigmatism by boring the holes round or by introducing compensators as is done in electron microscopes so that the major axis of the ellipse is not more than a few percent greater than the minor axis. The second limitation on the beam size is the spherical abberation that always exists in electromagnetic lenses. Let C_s be the spherical abberation constant; its value may not be reduced below about 3–5 cm for the focal lengths of 1–1.5 cm required in the electron probe. Let α be the semi-angle of convergence of the beam at the specimen as

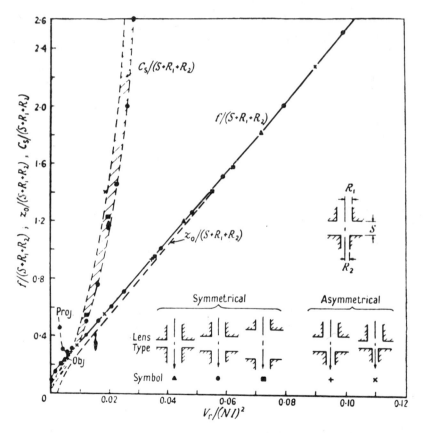

Fig. 7-6. Liebmann's curve for the spherical abberation constant of lenses like those of Fig. 7-5. The constant, C_s, is related to the bore radii, R_1 and R_2, the gap distance, S, the voltage of the electrons, V_r, and the number of ampere turns, NI, used in the lens coil.

shown in Fig. 7-5. The minimum spread of the beam due to spherical abberation is given by Eq. 7-1:

$$\delta = \tfrac{1}{2}C_s\alpha^3 \qquad\qquad (7\text{-}1)$$

where δ and C_s are in cm and α is in radians. The angle α is controlled by the limiting aperture that may be located in the gap of the second lens or above the second lens. For $\alpha = 2\times10^{-2}$ radians, and $C_s = 5$ cm, $\delta = \tfrac{5}{2}\times8\times10^{-6}$ cm $= 0.2$ microns. Castaing [1] states that δ should not be greater than 0.25 μ if a 1 μ beam is desired. The value above satisfies this criterion. The angle α should not be made any smaller than necessary to achieve the desired value of δ because the beam intensity reaching the specimen depends, of course, on the area of the limiting aperture and thus varies as α^2.

Determination of the spherical abberation constant for a given pole piece design is best accomplished using the curves published by Liebmann[4] who found that pole pieces of the type shown in Fig. 7-5 obeyed the curve shown in Fig. 7-6. Knowing the bore, R_1, R_2, gap S, number of ampere turns, NI, and focal length of the lens, f, one can quickly obtain C_s from the curve. The focal length is determined by the working distance, v, to the specimen, and the distance, u, to the image formed by the first lens; from the usual law of optics,

$$1/f = 1/u + 1/v$$

7.5. Limiting Apertures; Analogy to Light Optics

The two apertures have already been mentioned, but their analogy to the diaphragms used in ordinary optical microscopes should be shown. The first aperture immediately below the anode in Fig. 7-1 acts to pass only a limited amount of the intense central portion of the electron beam. Its size does not affect the final beam diameter. It may be considered as analogous to the field diaphragm in the optical microscope. The second aperture that may be located in or above the second electromagnetic lens acts to control the convergence angle of the beam at the specimen. Thus it is analogous to the aperture diaphragm in an optical microscope. Both these apertures will become contaminated gradually by the action of the electron beam and should be made of platinum so that they may be cleaned easily and frequently (at intervals of from 1 to 3 weeks).

Specimen Chamber

7.6. *Design of Chamber; Specimen Translation*

The specimen chamber is more than just a vacuum tight box at the end of the electron optics column: it is a precision instrument in itself. In order to make use of the 1 micron beam of electrons to examine specific areas on the specimen surface, one must be able to position the specimen to within 1 micron of the exact area desired. This means that each translation mechanism must be constructed very accurately. The sideways wobble of each translation must also be less than 2 microns if straight-line scanning of the specimen is to be possible. Finely machined dovetail ways and differential screws are required to accomplish the accurate translation desired. A further requirement on the specimen motion is that the plane of the specimen surface not be changed during translation. Specimen translation is accomplished from outside the vacuum column through rotating or sliding "O" ring seals. Motor drive for the specimen is desirable when distances of several hundred microns are to be scanned on the specimen surface. The drive speeds found convenient in the NRL instrument [2] are 3, 5, and 15 microns per minute.

The specimen chamber must have provision for taking the x-rays out of the vacuum system to the x-ray spectrometer. This may be a beryllium window if the spectrometer is to be operated in air, or it may be a thin Mylar window if the spectrometer is to be operated in partial vacuum for measuring the light elements.

7.7. *Electronic Scanning*

An alternative method for scanning the specimen is used by Duncumb.[5] Instead of translating the specimen, he sweeps the electron beam back and forth over the specimen to cover an area $\frac{1}{2}$ mm $\times \frac{1}{2}$ mm; it is the same technique used in scanning electron microscopes. Fig. 7-7 shows the arrangement schematically. D_1

and D_2 are deflecting coils; D_1 bends the beam to one side and D_2 bends it back so that it passes through the second aperture at an angle. A second set of coils at 90° with respect to those shown

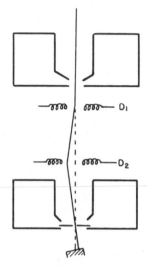

Fig. 7-7. Magnetic deflection of the electron beam by coils D_1 and D_2 as used at Cavendish Laboratory to sweep the beam across a small area of the specimen. A television type display tube synchronized with the beam sweep allows observation of composition differences in terms of brightness on the viewing screen.

sweeps the beam at right angles to the first direction. By making one set of coils sweep 100 times (or more) faster than the other set, an area is covered on the specimen surface. The x-ray output from the specimen may be used to modulate the brightness of a television-type display tube synchronized with the scanning of the specimen so that a picture of the specimen in terms of scattered x-rays is obtained. In fact, several pictures of the specimen in terms of several specific x-ray wavelengths may be obtained to show the relative distribution of different components. For quantitative analysis, the beam may be stopped on any desired area of the specimen.

x-Ray Optics

7.8. *Scanning Spectrometers*

The focal spot of the 1 micron electron beam is an ideal point source for the curved-crystal x-ray optics discussed in Chapter 3. A scanning, curved-crystal spectrometer such as the one shown in

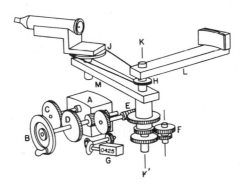

Fig. 7-8. The Naval Research Laboratory scanning curved-crystal spectrometer.

Fig. 7-8 may be used to measure the whole x-ray spectrum, or several fixed crystals and detectors as in Fig. 7-9 may be used to record the intensities of several elements continuously as the specimen is translated. The second method is often better because the nature of the specimen is often known before it is examined in the electron probe. What is then desired is the variation in composition of particular elements from place to place on the specimen. On the other hand, in airborne dusts, there may be no other means than the electron probe for determining the qualitative as well as the quantitative analysis of the particles, and so the scanning spectrometer is required.

For reflection optics, the crystals should be curved and ground after the method described in Sec. 3.6 of Chapter 3. Quartz, aluminum, or the alkali halides may be used depending on the resolution required. Quartz is a more perfect crystal and will allow resolution of the K_{α_1}, K_{α_2} doublet of copper for instance, but the spectrometer must be aligned very accurately with respect to the point source (about $\frac{1}{2}$ mm tolerance for the distance from the spectrometer axis to the point source). The quartz crystal "sees" only a band about 10 microns wide across the specimen; thus scanning the electron beam as mentioned in Sec. 7.7 would not be feasible with a quartz crystal. LiF is a convenient crystal just as in fluorescent x-ray spectroscopy. The peak diffracted intensity from LiF is perhaps no greater than with quartz but the line is broader so that the integrated intensity measured is several times greater than with quartz. For most problems, the resolution of LiF is sufficient just as in fluorescent x-ray spectroscopy. A scanning spectrometer of the type shown in Fig. 3-6d has been used by Fisher.[6] With this arrangement, the window between the specimen and the spectrometer need not be large because the crystal is moving away from the specimen in a straight line.

7.9. *Transmission Crystals for Short Wavelengths*

When fixed crystals and detectors are used as in Fig. 7-9, transmission curved crystals may be used to advantage for the short wavelength x-rays. It is then the planes normal to the surface of the crystal that are used for diffraction. The transmission crystal is curved to the diameter of the focusing circle but need not be ground to the radius of the circle. Just as with reflection crystals, only one wavelength will be diffracted for a given setting of the crystal. However, the diffracted radiation will continue to diverge, and a blade system as shown in Fig. 7-9 is required to prevent general transmitted radiation from reaching the detectors. One

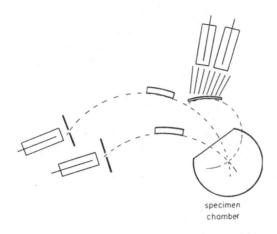

specimen
chamber

Fig. 7-9. x-Ray optics for simultaneous measurement of several wave-lengths. One transmission curved crystal and two reflection curved crystals are shown along with their respective detectors.

advantage of transmission crystals is that a much larger solid angle of the radiation from the point source is intercepted by the crystal especially for the short wavelengths when the θ angle is small. A second advantage is that θ angles approaching zero are possible while with a reflection crystal, the θ angle is limited at perhaps $7°$ by the physical contact of the crystal with the specimen chamber.

With LiF, the correct transmission crystal thickness for Mo K_α radiation at 0.7 A is about 2.8 mm.* This is a reasonable thickness to bend and no supporting frame for the crystal is required. The detectors used may be Geiger, proportional, or scintillation count-ers just as in fluorescent x-ray spectroscopy and the electronic circuitry is the same of course.

* For maximum diffracted intensity, the path length should be such that the transmitted intensity is $1/e$ times the incident intensity. In computing the thickness, the diffraction angle θ must be considered to obtain the path length.

7.10. *x-Ray Intensity Level*

The x-ray intensity available depends on the current in the electron beam and the operating voltage. For a one micron beam at 25–30 kev, the current is of the order of 1 microampere and the x-ray intensity from 100 % samples of medium elements like copper or iron is 10,000 cps or greater. The background is higher with electron excitation than with fluorescent excitation but line-to-background ratios of the order of 200 are easily obtained at the 100 % level. At a concentration of 0.1 % the line will therefore be only about 10 cps above a background of say 50 cps and this is about the limit of detectability. When a spot size of 3–5 microns may be tolerated, the beam current may reach 10 microamperes and the intensity approaches 100,000 cps for 100 % samples. However, the background increases correspondingly and the minimum concentration detectable is not improved appreciably.

7.11. *Effect of the Take-off Angle*

In Fig. 7-1 the specimen is shown inclined to the horizontal at an angle of 6°. The vertical divergence of the x-rays is 12° (6° below the horizontal and 6° above), but the average take-off angle is 6°. Some of the operating characteristics of the instrument depend on the average take-off angle. For instance, if the take-off angle is increased, there will be a more linear relation of intensity versus composition for light elements in a heavy matrix because the path length for the radiation in the specimen will be less. However, a larger take-off angle usually means that the specimen is more inclined to the horizontal and this may introduce difficulties mechanically by requiring inclination of the translation mechanism until it strikes the bottom of the lens coil. Some workers have extended the second lens pole piece below the bottom of the lens coil to allow more room to take the x-rays off above the horizontal. This means that the specimen may remain essentially in the horizontal plane but the x-ray spectrometers must then be inclined to correspond to the take-off angle.

The effect of take-off angle is illustrated by the intensity of chromium in iron. The iron *K* radiation excites the chromium spectrum strongly, and at a take-off angle of about 12°, 10 % chromium yields an intensity corresponding to that expected from 13 % chromium based on a comparison with a 100 % chromium sample. At a take-off angle of 6°, the chromium radiation is absorbed more in the iron, and the intensity versus composition is almost linear. For a light element not excited by the matrix, the intensity would be depressed further below the linear value with a 6° take-off angle than with a 12° take-off angle.

For ferromagnetic specimens inclined at a large angle to the horizontal there is an asymmetric interaction with the magnetic field of the lens that can be troublesome unless the working distance from the lens to the specimen is made large.

7.12. *Nondispersive Detection*

Nondispersive x-ray optics may replace the crystal spectrometers for some applications of the electron probe just as in fluorescence x-ray analysis. For instance, Macres [7] found it was possible in the copper-zinc system to use a 0.002 inch thick nickel filter to remove the $Zn\,K_\alpha$, $Zn\,K_\beta$, and $Cu\,K_\beta$ radiation selectively and then to measure only the $Cu\,K_\alpha$ radiation with a proportional counter and pulse amplitude discrimination circuit. For other systems it may not even be necessary to use a filter when pulse amplitude discrimination circuits are used. Adjustment of the operating voltage of the electron probe may also be used to discriminate against high atomic number elements; in the iron-tin system, the tin K spectrum will not be generated below 29 kev and nondispersive optics will detect only the iron radiation. It must always be kept in mind, however, that with electron excitation, the characteristic spectra appear above a high background. Since the background consists primarily of the same and neighboring wavelengths, it is not possible to eliminate all of it by pulse amplitude discrimination. Thus the limit of detectability is not improved appreciably with nondispersive optics even though the total intensity is increased several hundred times by eliminating the crystal diffraction. A possible exception occurs in the case of thin films of the order of a few hundred angstroms or isolated small particles in a very light matrix. Then the intensity from the desired element may be so low that nondispersive optics are required to detect it and the background will be relatively low because it comes from lower atomic number elements.

Viewing Microscope System

7.13. *Types of Objectives and Limits of Resolution*

Several types of viewing systems have been incorporated in the different electron probe instruments. Five types are illustrated in Fig. 7-10. Type *a* is a long working distance reflecting objective

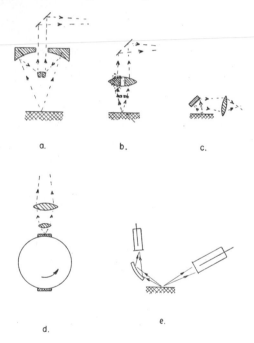

Fig. 7-10. Various designs for viewing systems used in electron probes. Type *a* is a reflecting objective mounted concentric with the electron beam; *b* is a refracting objective concentric with the electron beam; *c* is a mirror and transfer lens to remove the specimen image to an external microscope; *d* is a specimen mounted on a drum and turned from its position in the electron beam to a viewing position in front of an ordinary microscope; *e* is a specimen observed in terms of scattered x-rays or electrons instead of in terms of visible light.

mounted in the second lens pole piece. As used by Castaing,[1] the numerical aperture is about 0.4.and the resolution is less than 1 μ. Type b is a refracting objective mounted in the same way, but to achieve a reasonable working distance the numerical aperture is reduced to about 0.25 with a resulting resolution of only 1.2 μ. Both types a and b require that the specimen be normal to the electron optic and light optic axis in order to attain their theoretical resolution. In type c, a plane mirror is located above the specimen and reflects the image to a transfer lens inside the specimen chamber. An ordinary microscope then views the real image formed outside the specimen chamber. Physical limitations make the distance from the specimen to the transfer lens at least 1 cm. The numerical aperture is about 0.2 with a resulting resolution of about 1.5 μ. Type d as used by Mulvey is rather different from the others.[8] The specimen is mounted on a drum and rotated from outside the specimen chamber. When the drum is rotated, the specimen is removed from the electron beam and placed in front of a microscope objective mounted inside the vacuum chamber. A plane glass separates the objective from the rest of the microscope. By using an objective of 0.65 numerical aperture, a resolution of 0.5 μ may be achieved. In type e, the specimen is not viewed by visible light but rather in terms of scattered electrons or x-rays. Such an arrangement is used with the moving electron beam of Fig. 7-7.

There is no question but that the best optical resolution is desirable. However, there must be a balance between the instrumentation required and the results achieved. It is certainly more convenient to be able to view the specimen while it is in the electron beam than to have to remove it as with the type d arrangement above. If the specimen is photographed before placing it in the electron probe, it seems from experience that an optical resolution of 1–2 μ is sufficient to find the desired area. Thus the simple arrangement of type c seems adequate. With the electronic scanning described in Sec. 7.7 it might appear that optical viewing is unnecessary. However, the appearance of a specimen as seen by scattered electrons or x-rays is sometimes rather different from the appearance as seen by scattered light. At the present time, most workers are accustomed to the appearance of specimens in the light microscope and from this point of view, an optical viewing system is highly desirable.

Applications

7.14. *Suitable Specimens and Specimen Preparation*

Not all specimens suitable for fluorescent x-ray analysis are adaptable for examination in the electron probe. For instance, liquid specimens volatilize in the high vacuum required in the electron optics system. Some other materials may not be stable when irradiated with high energy electrons. The surface of the specimen must be smooth in order to prevent variations in x-ray output due to "shadowing" effects of surface projections (ordinary metallurgical polishing and etching is satisfactory for most specimens). Finally, the specimen must be electrically conducting or it must have a thin layer of metal evaporated onto it to make it conducting.

With the electron probe, the absorption effects between elements is small compared with usual fluorescent x-ray spectroscopy (see Sec. 5.5 for a discussion of the matrix effect). This is because only the surface layer is excited and the path length for the x-rays is a few microns instead of a few tenths of a millimeter. 100 % comparison samples of the elements of interest give a 1st order approximation for quantitative analysis. However, enhancement effects between elements is sometimes a problem. For instance, in a steel specimen containing 1 % titanium, the apparent titanium composition (by comparison with a 100 % titanium standard) was found to be 4 % titanium. This was due to the strong excitation of the titanium K spectrum by the Fe K_α line. Such discrepancies may be eliminated by comparison standards of approximately the same composition as the unknown; the standards should be mounted along with the unknown so that they may be measured under the same operating conditions. The enhancement effect is not easily eliminated when the elements in small segregations are excited by the surrounding matrix elements. In fact, accurate segregation composition cannot be determined *in situ* under such conditions, and it becomes necessary to extract the segregations from the matrix. Extraction replica techniques [9] as used for electron microscopy are useful for this purpose because they keep the segregations in the proper spatial arrangement. However, the collodion films used for electron micrsocopy do not hold up in the electron probe and it is better to extract the segregations, after etching the specimen, by pressing a polished piece of soft aluminum against the specimen surface. The segregations are imbedded in the soft aluminum and thus removed from the specimen surface. Also, the aluminum makes a conducting support for the segregations.

Regions smaller than the electron beam may be measured, but the answer is in terms of absolute quantity of the element which may be related to the percent composition only if the size of the region in question is known. Of course, relative composition of two elements contained in a sub-micron region may be determined *in situ* provided that neither of the elements is present in the surrounding matrix.

7.15. *Precipitates in Metals*

In metals, segregations or precipitates may be examined individually *in situ*, and variations in composition from one segregation to another may be determined. Fig. 7-11 shows carbides in

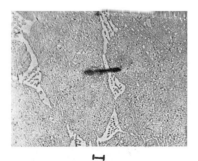

10µ

Fig. 7-11. Carbides in an iron matrix; the overall composition is 2.2 % carbon and 2.18 % nickel. With the electron probe, the nickel content was determined to be 0.75 % in the carbides and 2.6 % in the matrix. The scanning path of the electron beam is shown by the horizontal dark line near the center of the picture.

an iron matrix; the black line across the carbide is the trace left along the path of the electron beam. This trace is a contamination layer caused by interaction of the electron beam and carbonaceous molecules on the specimen surface (probably diffusion-pump oil molecules). It is very thin and usually does not interfere with the analysis. The specimen of Fig. 7-11 contained 2.2 % carbon and 2.18 % nickel with the balance iron. Electron probe analysis indicated a nickel content of 0.75 % in the carbides and 2.6 % in the matrix. Chemical analysis of the carbides after leaching them out of the matrix indicated 0.65 % nickel; the agreement is considered satisfactory. It can be seen in Fig. 7-11 that the carbides contain many small occluded matrix regions. The electron probe may be positioned to avoid these, but chemical analysis of the removed carbides probably includes these matrix regions and thus is in some error. Also, the electron probe determines any variation in composition from one particular carbide to another but chemical analysis does not. Similar analysis as shown in Table 7-1 was made on specimens where copper, cobalt, titanium, chromium, manganese, zirconium, molybdenum or other elements were substituted for the 2 % nickel. In some cases the carbides were richer in the addition elements and in some cases poorer than the matrix.

TABLE 7-1

Comparison of Electron Probe and Chemical Analysis for Various Elements in Iron and Iron Carbide [a]

Element added	Matrix		Carbides	
	Electron probe	Chemical	Electron probe	Chemical
Ni	2.6 %	—	0.75 %	0.65 %
Cu	2.5	2.7 %	0.2	0.25
Co	1.0	0.8	0.4	0.35
Mn	0.6	0.75	2.3	—
Cr	0.25	0.15	1.6	1.5
V	—	0.1	0.9	—
Mo	—	0.19	3.0	4.3
Zr	—	0.13	—	0.3

[a] In each specimen, the carbon content is about 2 % and the iron content is 95–97 %.

7.16. *Intermetallic Diffusion*

Intermetallic diffusion is readily studied in the electron probe.[10] There are two cases of interest. For alloys where distinct intermetallic phases occur over certain composition ranges, the electron probe allows the sharpness of the phase boundary to be determined directly. Fig. 7-12 shows two idealized situations. In Fig. 7-12a the

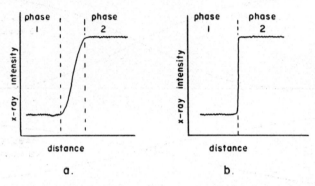

Fig. 7-12. Idealized phase boundaries in alloys. On the left, the x-ray intensity goes up gradually in the diffusion region, but on the right it goes up abruptly where the two phases come together.

change at the boundary between phase 1 and phase 2 is continuous and extends over a range of 5 microns; in Fig. 7-12b the change at the boundary is abrupt within the resolution of the instrument.

For other alloy systems there is a continuous range of solid solution and the electron probe may be used to show the extent of diffusion as a function of time or temperature or both. An example is the titanium-zirconium system and Fig. 7-13 shows typical diffusion curves for three different heat treatments. From such curves, the diffusion coefficients may be calculated.

Another example is the grain boundary diffusion of zinc in silver. Metallography using radioactive traces indicates a preferential diffusion along the grain boundaries but it does not indicate the extent of diffusion that exists away from the boundaries. Fig. 7-14 shows a photograph of the zinc-silver system * with a grain boundary outlined by the line of pits. The specimen had been

* From work being done at NRL by Dr. M. R. Achter.

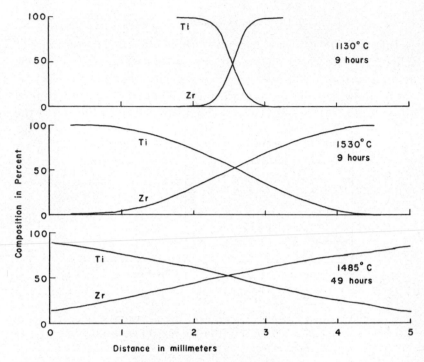

Fig. 7-13. The titanium-zirconium system shows a continuous range of solid solution. With the electron probe, the extent of diffusion is easily determined for various heat treatments, and diffusion coefficients are readily calculated from the shape and slope of the curves.

Fig. 7-14. In the zinc-silver system, there is preferred diffusion along grain boundaries under certain conditions. The grain boundary normal to the surface is outlined by the dark line of pits. Scanning across the boundary along the line $A–A$ indicated about 1 % zinc at the boundary and only 0.3 % zinc at a distance of some 25 microns away from the boundary.

prepared by heating pure silver in a partial pressure of zinc vapor for 60 hours at 650° C. Visually, the diffusion of the zinc into the silver extended about 0.014 inches. In the electron probe, it was found to extend beyond 0.020 inches. At a distance of 0.0165 inches from the surface, as shown at $A-A$ in Fig. 7-14, the zinc content at the grain boundary was found to be about 1 % while away from the grain boundary it was less than 0.3 %, verifying the assumption that diffusion proceeds more rapidly along the grain boundaries.

7.17. *Change in Concentration near Free Surface*

Depletion of one or more elements in a matrix near a surface subject to corrosion action is another example of the usefulness of the electron probe. Fig. 7-15 shows the cross section of a corroded

Fig. 7-15. Cross section of an 18 % chromium-8 % nickel stainless steel tube after corrosion by liquid lithium; the steel is on the right side of the picture. Electron probe scanning along the line $A-A$ indicated chemical depletion of chromium for a distance of 5 to 10 microns below the surface as shown in Fig. 7-16.

surface of 18 % chromium, 8 % nickel stainless steel after attack by liquid lithium metal.[11] The chromium is depleted for a distance of 5–10 microns below the surface as shown in Fig. 7-16. To make these measurements, the arrangement of Fig. 7-9 was employed for simultaneous determination of chromium, nickel, and iron. It would have been much more tedious to perform this analysis with a scanning spectrometer where each of the three elements would

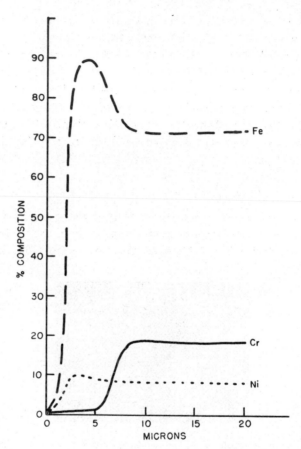

Fig. 7-16. Iron, nickel, and chromium composition as a function of distance below the corroded surface of Fig. 7-15. The chromium is depleted for a distance of 5 to 10 microns. (The hump in the iron and nickel curves comes about from normalizing the sum of the individual components to 100 %.)

have had to be measured individually for each position of the specimen in steps of 1 micron for 40 microns.

7.18. *Segregations in Minerals*

In minerals and ores there are often small discrete regions that are difficult to separate from the matrix for chemical analysis. One of the first minerals examined with the electron probe [11] was a good example of this. In the copper-iron mineral chalcopyrite, areas of a birefringent material had often been observed. They occurred as lightning-like streaks some 10–15 microns wide as shown by the white areas in Fig. 7-17. From their birefringent properties they

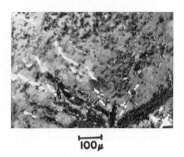

100μ

Fig. 7-17. The white streaks are an iron rich phase in chalcopyrite ($CuFeS_2$) mineral. Their composition was measured accurately for the first time by using an electron probe. They contain about 55 % iron and less than 5 % copper and are probably a sulfide.

had been tentatively identified as the mineral valleriite which contains iron and copper in the ratio 2 : 1. No chemical analysis had ever been possible. To examine the specimen in the electron probe required special technique because a conducting layer had to be evaporated over the polished surface. It was realized that this would prevent recognition of the streaks which were distinguishable from the matrix only in polarized light. Therefore the specimen was photographed before coating the surface and the location of streaks noted with respect to certain scratches and pits. After coating the surface with a thin layer of evaporated manganese, the specimen was placed in the electron probe and set at the proper position with respect to the indexed scratches and pits that could be seen through the evaporated layer. The copper and iron intensities were measured at about a dozen such positions and were always different than in the surrounding matrix. Quantitative estimates of the copper and iron content were made by comparison with the known copper-iron minerals shown in Table 7-2. The x-ray intensities did not correspond to those from a known specimen of valleriite. Instead the streaks appeared to contain almost no copper

TABLE 7-2

Composition of Copper-Iron Minerals

		Iron			Copper		
Mineral	Formula	x-Ray intensity	% x-ray	% formula	x-Ray intensity	% x-ray	% formula
Chalcopyrite	$CuFeS_2$	126 cps	std.	30.4	160	std.	34.6
Cubanite	$CuFe_2S_3$	164	40	41.2	98	22	23.4
Valleriite	$Cu_{2-3}Fe_4S_7$	110	26.2	35–39	120	29	20–22
Pyrite	FeS	110	std.	46.5	0	—	0
Unknown	~ FeS	212	51 [a] 58 [b]	63.5?	15–30	0–5 [a] 0–5 [b]	0

[a] Comparison with chalcopyrite.
[b] Comparison with pyrite.

but agreed approximately with a FeS composition.*

Many mineralogical problems are not as difficult as the example above, but the advantage of the electron probe for examination of heterogeneous specimens encountered in minerals and ores is obvious.

7.19.   Possible Biological Applications

The electron probe is also useful for biological problems. For instance in the *tibia* bone from a rat, the calcium content was measured in a section going from bone into cartilage. It ranged from an estimated 30 weight percent in small regions of the bone proper to effectively zero percent in the newly formed cartilage. It was also observed that the calcium occurred principally in the region between the bone cells themselves.

Heavy metal staining of biological specimens may be used to show the variation in cell structure. Techniques for staining with phosphotungstic acid or osmium have been developed for electron microscopy for similar purposes. The electron probe is more suit-

* Sulfur could not be measured in the electron probe but a sulfide appeared to be the likely compound. From the iron intensity it could be estimated that the compound was closer to FeS than to Fe_2S.

able, however, for measuring the quantitative distribution of the staining provided that the resolution of 1 micron is sufficient.

7.20.   *Conclusion*

In summing up the discussion of the electron probe it should be stated that it is a relatively new instrument and all of its potentialities are far from being known. It appears to have a great future because there are few techniques that can detect of the order of 10^{-13} to 10^{-14} grams of an element or can perform chemical analysis on areas as small as 1 micron.

References

1. R. Castaing, *Thesis*, University of Paris (1951).
2. L. S. Birks and E. J. Brooks, *Rev. Sci. Instr.* **28**, 709 (1957).
3. M. Bricka and H. Bruck, *Ann. de Radioelectricité* 111, **14**, 339 (1948).
4. G Liebmann, *Proc. Phys. Soc. (London)* **B68**, 737 (1955).
5. V. E. Cosslett and P. Duncumb, *Electron Microscopy, Proc. Stockholm Conf.* (1956).
6. R. M. Fisher, *Electron Microscopy Soc. of America 15th Ann. Meeting*, Cambridge, Mass. (1957).
7. V. Macres, *Office Naval Research Conf.*, Washington, D.C., (Feb. 1958).
8. T. Mulvey, *Office Naval Research Conf.*, Washington, D.C., (Feb. 1958).
9. R. M. Fisher, *Am. Society Testing Materials, Spec. Tech. Publ.*, No. 155, (1954) p. 49.
10. R. Castaing and A. Guinier, *Anal. Chem.* **25**, 724 (1953).
11. L. S. Birks and E. J. Brooks, *Denver Research Conf.*, Aug. (1957).

CONSTANT POTENTIAL OPERATION
OF X-RAY POWER SUPPLIES

App. 1.1.

A rectified AC power supply may be converted to a constant potential power supply with resulting gain in effective output of the x-ray tube as discussed in Sec. 2.9 of Chapter 2. To accomplish the change to constant potential, a single stage of resistance-capacitance filtering or inductance-capacitance filtering is added, as shown in Fig. App. 1-1. For the commonly used x-ray tubes operat-

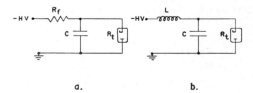

a.   b.

Fig. App. 1-1. Filtering of the high voltage supplied to an x-ray tube in order to obtain constant potential operation; a, resistance-capacitance filtering; b, inductance-capacitance filtering. R_T represents the x-ray tube and its electrical resistance.

ing at 60 kev peak and 50 milliamps, the power dissipated in the tube is

$$0.7 \times 60 \times 10^3 \times 50 \times 10^{-3} = 2100 \text{ watts.}$$

To operate the filter, extra power is required, and the x-ray transformer must be capable of delivering this extra power if the full advantage of the constant potential arrangement is to be achieved.

App. 1.2.

As an example of the principles involved, we may consider Fig. App. 1-1a and assume the following values:

$$R_F = 2 \text{ megohms} = 2 \times 10^6 \text{ ohms}$$
$$C \;\; = 10 \text{ microfarads} = 10 \times 10^{-6} \text{ farads}$$
$$R_T = 1.2 \text{ megohms} = 1.2 \times 10^6 \text{ ohms}$$

The value for R_T is obtained by assuming 60 kev and 50 ma in the x-ray tube and using the ordinary relation $R = V/I$, where V is the potential and I is the current. Although full-wave rectified AC potential is not strictly a sine wave, it may be taken as such for a first order approximation. The frequency, f, will be 120 cycles rather than the 60 cycles of the transformer. More exact treatment of the problem may be found in electrical engineering texts.[1] In order to determine the current which will be drawn by the filter resistor R_F, we must consider the impedance of the whole circuit and must therefore know the impedance, Z_1, of the parallel circuit containing C and R_T. It is given according to standard AC circuit analysis by the equation

$$Z_1 = (R_T - iR_T^2 C\omega)/[1 + (R_T C\omega)^2] \qquad \text{(App. 1-1)}$$

where $\omega = 2\pi \text{ frequency} = 2\pi\,120 = 755$, and i is the imaginary number $\sqrt{-1}$. Substituting the proper values for R_T, C, and ω and solving for Z_1, we obtain

$$Z_1 = 0.0146 - i133 \text{ ohms}$$

The impedance of the whole circuit becomes $Z = R_F + Z_1$. Since the imaginary part is very small compared to the real part, we may approximate Z as $Z = 2 \times 10^6$ ohms; that is, just the resistance of the filter resistor. The current drawn by the filter resistor becomes

$$I_F = V/R_F = 60 \times 10^3/2 \times 10^6 = 30 \times 10^{-3} \text{ amperes.}$$

The power dissipated in the filter resistor becomes

$$0.7 \times 60 \times 10^3 \times 30 \times 10^{-3} = 1260 \text{ watts.}$$

Assuming that the x-ray tube continues to operate at its original power of 2100 watts, the total power drawn from the x-ray transformer will be approximately 3360 watts because the capacitance will draw less than 1 watt.

App. 1.3.

To discuss the effect of the filter in smoothing the voltage supplied to the x-ray tube, we now consider the filter resistor and the capacitance as a unit, and using the common equation for resistance-capacitance filters, we obtain the AC component across the x-ray tube from the equation,

$$V_{AC\ out} = V_{AC\ in}/R_F C\omega \qquad \text{(App. 1-2)}$$

Substituting the values above, we find $V_{AC\ out} = 3.7$ volts. This is a very small value for the AC component. The DC component across the x-ray tube will be almost the full 60 kev if there is negligible leakage in the condenser.

App. 1.4.

The nature of the filter components should be mentioned. The capacitor must be able to withstand the full 60 kev potential and should, if possible, be mounted in transformer oil to prevent corona. Its size will be between one and two cubic feet. It is lethal when charged, and a bleeder resistance of perhaps 500 to 1000 megohms should be placed across it so the charge will drain off when the circuit is turned off. The resistance R_F must be able to dissipate the 1260 watts and to withstand the 60 kev potential. It will be large physically and some form of cooling may be required.

App. 1.5.

If the inductance-capacitance filter of Fig. App. 1-1b is used, the minimum inductance value is obtained from the equation,

$$L_{min} = R_T/1160 \qquad \text{(App. 1-3)}$$

where it is assumed that full-wave rectified potential is supplied at 60 cycles. Substituting the value of R_T, the minimum inductance is found to be about 1050 henries. As with the other components, the size of this inductance will be several cubic feet.

Reference

1. F. E. Terman, *Radio Engineers Handbook*, McGraw-Hill, New York, 1943.

PREPARATION OF PLASTICALLY CURVED CRYSTALS

App. 2.1.

In plastic curving of single crystals, damage to the crystal or fracture may result from improper treatment. It is necessary to reorient the crystalline planes along the arc of a circle by realigning the mosaic blocks but without introducing large angular misorientations at any point in the crystal. In alkali halides, the individual mosaic blocks are of the order of 500 A in size and misoriented with respect to each other, on the average, by about 10 seconds of arc or greater. If there were no misorientation between mosaic blocks, curving the crystal to a radius of 10 cm would introduce only 0.1 seconds of arc difference of orientation between adjacent mosaic blocks of 500 A size. Thus it is apparent that curving the crystal should not cause any noticeable increase in mosaic spread, and indeed it does not introduce any increase in diffracted line breadth if proper precautions are followed.

App. 2.2.

There are two steps in preparing curved crystals for best focusing action according to the method of Johansson.[1] Suppose that a 10 cm radius focusing circle is to be used. First, the crystal must be curved to a radius of 20 cm, and second, the concave surface must be ground to a radius of 10 cm to fit the focusing circle as shown schematically in Fig. App. 2-1. It should be mentioned that the order of curving and grinding may be interchanged, that is, the crystal may first be ground to a radius of 20 cm and then the concave surface curved to a radius of 10 cm. This is often the more convenient method for elastically curved crystals, but for plastic curving, it may result in less uniform curvature. The length of the crystal is not limited theoretically, but practically it is limited to about 2 inches for a 10 cm focusing circle and to about 3 inches for a 20 cm focusing circle.

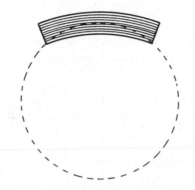

Fig. App. 2-1. The first step in preparing a plastically curved reflection crystal is bending to a radius equal to the diameter of the focusing circle (shown as the broken line).

App. 2.3.

The first step in preparing the crystal is to cleave a suitable thickness—about $\frac{1}{8}$ inch for a 10 cm circle and about $\frac{1}{16}$ inch for a 20 cm circle. The surface of the cleavage section may be smoothed if necessary by abrading on 400 Aloxite paper or similar abrasive and etching to remove worked material. A 50-50 alcohol-water mixture is suitable for NaCl; a solution of dilute hydrochloric acid plus dilute acetic acid plus a few tenths percent ferric chloride is suitable for LiF. Care should be taken in abrading not to cut the crystal at an appreciable angle to the cleavage planes.

Next the crystal is heated slowly on a flat surface to the temperature of the curved die—approximately 300° C. When it has reached this temperature, it is transferred to the die as shown in Fig. App. 2-2a. A ball made by winding asbestos cord around a tennis ball to a thickness of about $\frac{1}{2}$ inch makes a suitable device for curving the hot crystal.[2] It should be pressed down slowly in the center at first as shown in Fig. App. 2-2b and gradually worked out toward the ends as in Fig. App. 2-2c until the entire length of the crystal is uniformly curved to the die. All of this should be done on a hotplate or similar heating unit so that there is no cooling of

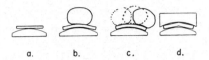

Fig. App. 2-2. Steps in curving a crystal plastically; a, the curved die and the flat crystal are heated on a hot plate; b, a ball of asbestos twine is used to press down on the center of the crystal and start the curvature; c, the ball is gradually pressed harder and rolled out towards the ends of the crystal to complete the curving; d, an improper bend may result if matching dies are used for curving a crystal because the three point contact results in the "peaked roof" effect that is extremely difficult to remove.

the crystal or die until the curvature is attained.

Some workers have used two dies as shown in Fig. App. 2-2d, but this is not recommended because the initial three-point contact causes a sharp initial bend at the center of the crystal, and subsequent curvature does not remove the "peaked roof" effect completely; the result is that the crystal may show a doubling of the focused diffraction line.

After the crystal has been curved to the die, it is allowed to cool slowly with the die, and during this period, a concave die may be placed on top of it if one is available. However, it is not necessary with LiF because there is only slight distortion on cooling. With NaCl, there may be continued distortion even after cooling, and in one case, it was noted that an unrestrained NaCl crystal initially curved to a 40 cm die continued to bend over a period of a week and finally reached a curvature of 33 cm.

App. 2.4.

The crystal should be cemented to a metal form cut to fit the convex surface as shown in Fig. App. 2-3a. Beeswax dissolved in benzene makes a suitable cement, or picene may be used before the crystal has cooled. The metal form is held in a vise and the center of the crystal is cut down with coarse abrasive paper or even a coarse rasp file until something like the proper curvature is reached as shown in Fig. App. 2-3b. Then a die of the proper grinding radius is positioned against backing strips S and S' as shown in Fig. App. 2-3c and allowed to rest on the crystal. Abrasive paper is drawn between the die and the crystal to work the surface to the proper curvature; coarse abrasive should be used first and then

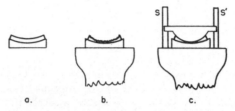

Fig. App. 2-3. After curving, the crystal is mounted on a concave form so that its inner surface may be ground to the radius of the focusing circle. On the left, the crystal is shown before grinding. In the center view, the form is held in a vise and a rough sutting to an approximate radius is accomplished with a rasp file. In the right hand view, the final grinding is done by holding a die of the proper curvature lightly against the crystal and against the vertical guide rods; abrasive paper is drawn between the die and the crystal until the proper curvature is obtained.

the finishing is done with fine abrasive at about the 400 Aloxite grade. After the crystal has been cut, it is given a light etch to remove worked material as discussed in Sec. App. 2.3. It is then ready to use.

App. 2.5.

The procedures described above yield a high percentage of excellent curved crystals provided that the starting material is a good quality single crystal without excessive lineage markings or obvious misoriented macroscopic regions. Testing of the crystal after the curving is easy, and only suitable crystals should be ground and used. To test the crystal, the reflection of a light may be observed visually. The curved crystal acts just as a curved mirror and will reflect an image of the light. The image should be undistorted for all parts of the surface. If the ends of the crystal are not curved sufficiently, the image will change size when reflected from these portions. The actual radius of curvature may be measured by reflecting a distant source such as the sun. A line will be formed as shown in Fig. App. 2-4 at a distance equal to $R/2$ where R is the radius of curvature of the crystal. Any crystal which shows a deviation of more than 5 per cent from the desired value should be discarded.

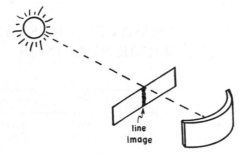

Fig. App. 2-4. Testing the curvature of the crystal may be done by using it to focus the light from a distant source such as the sun on an opaque white screen held slightly below the direct line of sight. If the curvature is uniform, a rather sharp line image will be formed when the crystal-to-screen distance is equal to half the bending radius.

USEFUL ANALYZER CRYSTALS
AND THEIR SPACINGS

Crystal	Planes	d spacing
LiF	(200)	2.01
EDDT [a]	(020)	4.38
Aluminum	(111)	2.31
NaCl	(200)	2.81
KCl	(200)	3.14
KBr	(200)	3.29
Quartz	($10\bar{1}1$)	3.35
ADP [b]	(200)	3.75
Quartz	($10\bar{1}0$)	4.25
Pentaerythritol	(002)	4.38
ADP [b]	(110)	5.31
Oxalic acid	(001)	5.85
Graphite	(001)	6.69
Mica	(002)	9.9
Silver acetate	(001)	10.0

[a] Ethylenediamine d-tartrate
[b] Ammonium dihydrogen phosphate

The Bragg angle θ is obtained from the equation $n\lambda = 2d \sin \theta$ where λ is the wavelength in A.

For an excellent tabulation of wavelength, the reader is referred to *Handbuch der Physik*, Volume 30. Shorter tabulations that are sufficient for much practical work may be found in *The Handbook of Chemistry and Physics*, any volume.

AUTHOR INDEX

SUBJECT INDEX